SCIENCE VS EVOLUTION

DATE DUE	

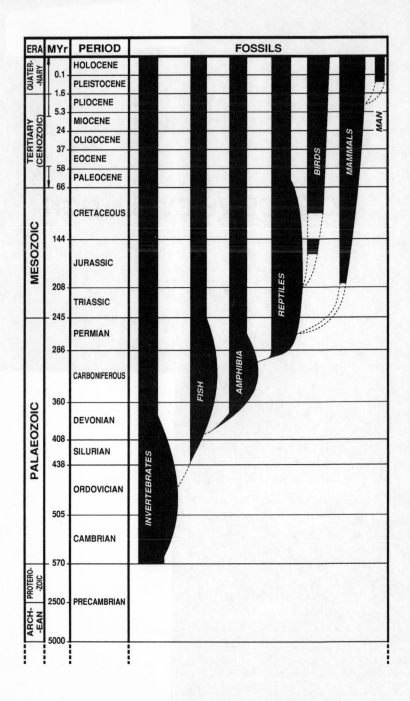

A typical geological column of evolution

SCIENCE
VS
EVOLUTION

Malcolm Bowden

SOVEREIGN PUBLICATIONS
P. O. Box 88
Bromley
Kent
BR2 9PF

SOVEREIGN PUBLICATIONS
P. O. Box 88, Bromley, Kent, BR2 9PF
© Malcolm Bowden 1991

First published 1991

British Library Cataloguing in Publication Data available

ISBN 0 9506042 3 2

Printed in Great Britain by the Bath Press, Avon

ACKNOWLEDGEMENTS

I would like to thank Mr. Peter Senior for help with obtaining papers. Special thanks are due to Dr. Arthur Jones for reading the manuscript and for the help given on many biological items, in particular the subjects of cortical inheritance, cichlid fishes and the dispersion of animals. I am also indebted to Andrew, who much improved the quality of many of the diagrams in the book. Last, but by no means least, I must thank my good friend and widely loved Esmé Geering who took on the onerous task of reading the proofs to correct my many errors of spelling and grammar.

DEDICATION

I would finally like to pay tribute to the many creationists who have provided information throughout the years. The material contained within this work is the result of the accumulated evidence patiently gathered by them and then circulated, often involving considerable time and expense and sometimes against opposition: all I have done is merely to arrange it in the order that is presented to the reader. It is to these many tireless workers who seek to present the true facts to the general public that this book is sincerely dedicated.

COPYRIGHT

EMPHASISED QUOTATIONS

Unless otherwise noted, all emphasised words or passages within a quotation are made by the author of this book.

LIST OF ILLUSTRATIONS

Frontispiece — The Geological Column of Evolution

CONTENTS

SECTION II — BIOLOGY

SECTION III — PHYSICS

SECTION IV — THE RISE OF EVOLUTION

FOREWORD

In his two previous books, 'Ape-men: Fact or Fallacy?' and 'The Rise of the Evolution Fraud', Malcolm Bowden demonstrated his ability to thoroughly research technical subjects and then put them into writing that is both interesting and comprehensible to scientists and laymen alike. This book, 'Science vs, Evolution', proves to be as successful in all respects. In his latest publishing venture, Bowden thoroughly covers the subject of science vs. evolution and finds the evolution theory to be deficient in every respect labelling it 'the greatest scientific hoax of all time.' This reminds one of the statement of Soren Lovtrup, although most definitely an evolutionist, that 'someday the Darwinian myth will be ranked the greatest deceit in the history of science' (Darwinism: The Refutation of a Myth' Croome Helm, New York, 1987, p422) Of considerable help to the layman is the fact that not only is Bowden's book well illustrated, but each point is discussed in easily comprehensible terms.

In all the history of science, no theory has been more dogmatically promoted as established fact than the theory of evolution, even though it would of necessity involve events that were unobservable and unrepeatable and is, in fact, contradicted by a mass of circumstantial evidence. As Bowden documents, evolutionists employ various stratagems to hide the weakness of their theory, including vague phraseology, false analogies, converting assumption into 'facts', concealing contradictory evidence, and attacking straw men. While evolutionists in general decry the state of science education in most countries, certainly that in the U.S., one of the reasons that evolution theory enjoys the credibility that it does, is due to the fact that most people understand neither the theory of evolution not the actual nature of the scientific evidence that so powerfully militates against it. In 'Science vs. Evolution', Bowden makes an effective effort to correct both deficiencies.

'Science vs. Evolution' contains a wealth of highly interesting and relevant material, is scientifically accurate, and is written in an easily readable popular style. It will be of help and interest to all except for those who wish to listen only to hymns of praise to Darwinism.

Dr. Duane T. Gish
Director — Creation Research Institute
California U.S.A.

INTRODUCTION

In 1859 Charles Darwin published his book 'The Origin of Species' in which he provided evidence to show how the very diverse animals now existing had evolved from earlier primitive life over a long period of time. He considered that this had occurred by the process of the fittest members of a group surviving in the fierce competition for the available food resources. These fitter members would have certain characteristics enabling them to survive, which they would pass on to their offspring. They in turn would pass these features, further developed, on to their offspring. Thus over a long period of time, a wide variety of characteristics would arise, resulting in the enormous diversity of forms of life that we see today.

Such was the main outline of his theory. The question was; could this be demonstrated by direct evidence?

Unfortunately for Darwin, the answer was *no*.

Despite numerous experiments on animals, the extent of the variation he required was not achieved. A species could not be induced to change into another species. Neither could any mechanism be found whereby a parent could pass any newly learnt characteristic on to its offspring by inheritance. The whole basis of his theory was thus found to be inadequate and doubts about its validity began to be expressed.

In the face of this evidence, the theory was modified to Neo-Darwinism. This relies upon particular types of offspring known as genetic 'mutations' to effect permanent changes in a species. In all species, there is variation amongst the members, but occasionally an individual is noticeably different to the general stock, and these are called 'mutations'. To give an example, in both human and animal populations a very small percentage lack the normal colouring pigments in their skin cells and are known as 'albinos'.

It is acknowledged by evolutionists that virtually all mutants suffer from deficiencies. However, it is claimed that under certain conditions of the environment, they may nevertheless occasionally confer a benefit to the individual, enabling him to survive and thus pass the new characteristic on to his offspring. In this way, species are said to diverge due to these chance mutations acting over millions of years.

This then is the most widely accepted basis of the present day theory of evolution, which is considered to be an incontrovertible 'fact' by many. There is however an enormous amount of evidence against it, which receives very little publicity. What follows is only a small part of the total evidence, but a number of the topics examined are the very ones which are put forward in support of the theory. Close examination of all such seemingly convincing evidence, however, will show the serious flaws that it contains.

In this publication, the facts are presented as simply as possible, whilst still providing answers to more technical questions. Inevitably, many aspects merge with those that will receive a fuller treatment in a second future volume on the 'Scientific Evidence Supporting Genesis' which is in course of preparation.

It is hoped that this work will be read by those who have doubts about the validity of the theory. It should also be a handbook for those who wish to refute a theory that has had so much publicity for over one hundred and thirty years — publicity that I hope to demonstrate is undeserved.

I would at this point like to comment on the geological dating scales used. In illustrations and text in this work referring to the ages of the various strata, I have used the values of millions of years as given by the latest publications by evolutionists. I have used these dates so that there may be some common basis on which discussion of a sequence of events may be carried on with the opponents, even though the dates help to show inconsistencies within the theory itself. I would emphasise that I do not accept that these spans of millions of years have any validity, as I consider that the weight of scientific evidence strongly indicates that the age of the earth should be measured not in millions of years but in a few thousand years only.

In the reading of this book it will become apparent that I am critical of 'evolutionists', at times seemingly a little severe. I would emphasise that the evolutionists that I am referring to are *not* the multitude of ordinary people who believe that evolution it true, for they have been indoctrinated with the theory in schools and colleges where no contrary evidence is presented.

The evolutionists towards whom my criticisms are directed are that small group of people who write the books, edit the papers and produce the programmes in which the theory is presented in a very convincing manner. Usually they are well aware of the shortcomings of the theory, yet, despite this, continue to encourage its widespread propagation and discourage the expression of all contrary views. I would ask the reader to bear with my approach until he reaches the end of the book, when he may be more prepared to agree that my criticisms are well warranted.

SECTION I — GEOLOGY

In looking for evidence that evolution has occurred, researchers investigate various fields of science and any results which support the theory are frequently given considerable publicity. Information from genetics, similarities, adaptations etc., may *infer* that evolution *could* have taken place. Even if this evidence was very convincing, however, it would not prove that evolution did actually occur. Only the fossils in the geological strata can provide more direct evidence that it actually *did* take place. It is for this reason that the geological evidence is crucial and therefore the subject that we will examine first.

A. EVOLUTIONARY CHARTS

Invariably, in all textbooks dealing with evolution, a chart of the geological strata with the main groups of fossils they contain is given, and a typical diagram is shown in the Frontispiece. It has been positioned there for easy reference as the names of the geological strata will often be referred to.

All of these diagrams assume that the deepest strata would have been laid down first, each stratum consisting of material washed from the land into the sea where it would settle out. As time went by, further deposits would be laid on top like layers in a cake. Whilst they were being deposited, various animals would die and fall into the settling material, their bones would be preserved and gradually turned into stone to become fossils. It is these fossilised remains of animals that are found in the strata today. Thus each stratum is said to contain a fossilised sample of animals and plants which existed at that time.

These charts show the small sea creatures at the bottom in the oldest and deepest rocks and as you go up the column, other fossils appear in a seeming progression until you reach man at the top in the most recently deposited strata. The geological evidence is claimed to support evolution as the fossils are found in exactly the same sequence as they evolved, i.e. there is the same progression from sea creatures through the various groups as life developed later on land to eventually produce the numerous animals now existing. On the left hand side of the Frontispiece appear the ages when geologists believe the various strata were laid down. The datings will vary between charts as each expert will use different values based on various authorities. Those shown are based on the the 1983 American time scale.

Charts such as these appear so frequently that they are taken by many as well founded upon facts and incontrovertible evidence for evolution. Now let us look at some of the criticisms which can be made of these charts.

1. HOW THE CHART IS COMPOSED.

The first thing which must be emphasized is that these charts are composed by piecing together the strata from various continents. It has been estimated that only 0.4% of the world's land surface have the main divisions in their correct order, and even then a number of the sub-divisions are missing. 77% has seven or more of the strata systems missing, whilst 99.6% has at least one missing system [1]. This gives some indication of just how incomplete the geological record is from an evolutionary standpoint. The gaps between the various strata can be large. For example, the Cretaceous may lie directly on top of the Devonian, all the 'ages' between being missing. Indeed, *any one* of the different strata can be found lying immediately on top of the Precambrian stratum (which has no animal fossils), *all* the intervening ages being completely 'absent'.

The usual explanation given is that these intermediate strata have been eroded. Yet if this were so, we would expect to see the lower layer at different angles to the upper (an unconformity). But frequently they are both parallel to each other (i.e. they conform) and it is obvious that they were laid consecutively in a fairly short period of time, before any erosion of the lower strata had taken place (Fig.1).

It must be emphasized that *the label given to a stratum depends entirely on the fossils it contains*. Thus, those with a large number of fishes were called Devonian, those with coal measures were called Carboniferous, etc. As it is claimed the strata were laid down slowly over millions of years, when contradictory evidence is discovered, highly speculative explanations have to be resorted to, and little or no supporting evidence is provided. Indeed, there are so many 'problems' with these simplified charts, that it is not too great an exaggeration to say that they bear little resemblance to the strata as they are discovered in the field.

In the following simplified illustration it will be seen just how

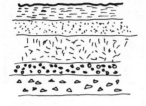

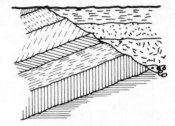

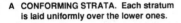

A CONFORMING STRATA. Each stratum is laid uniformly over the lower ones.

B UNCONFORMING STRATA. Older strata are laid, tilted and eroded. Later strata laid at a different angle to the earlier ones.

Fig. 1 Geological conformity and unconformity.

composite the column sequence is, and the evolutionary basis on which it has been erected.

Take three areas, A, B and C, (Fig. 2A) that have a series of strata which contain a variety of fossils, in particular specialised fossils of a mammal and a fish, each of which the evolutionist believed only inhabited the earth for a comparatively short period of time. Fossils of this sort are known as Index Fossils, for they are said to provide a distinctive label for the stratum in which they are found. In area A the mammal is found near the bottom of the strata sequence, and at site B near the top. Similarly in area B, the fish is found near the bottom, and in area C near the top.

On the assumption that the index fossils were laid down during the same geological period, the separate areas would be correlated as shown in Fig. 2B. They will then be combined to give one continuous column as in Fig. 2C. This is the way in which the fossils have been interpreted in constructing the whole of the geological column, and the evolutionary assumption (that many animals evolved and later became extinct), that forms the whole basis for the compilation of the column, cannot be emphasized enough.

Flood geology.

There is however a perfectly satisfactory alternative explanation. This is the interpretation given by those who contend that a world wide flood is able to account for the dispersal of the majority of the various fossils in the strata. The explanation is that all the animals were living at the same time and were washed into different areas and at different stages of the flood by the rising waters that gradually overwhelmed the whole earth. The whole subject is one for a subsequent creationist book, but Fig. 2D shows how in general the position of the fossils could have been laid down in one great Flood.

2A   THE STRATA AS DISCOVERED:-

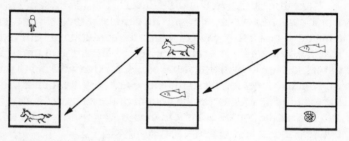

2B   THE ASSUMPTIONS ARE MADE:-

"Index fossils" are assumed to have existed for a short period of time in the evolutionary time scale, and the strata are therefore considered to have been laid down at the same time

2C   THE STRATA ARE CORRELATED:-

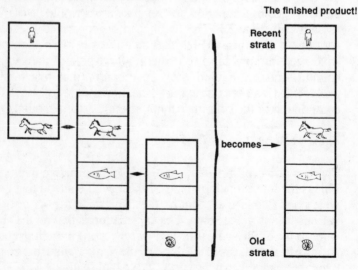

Fig. 2 How the geological column was compiled.

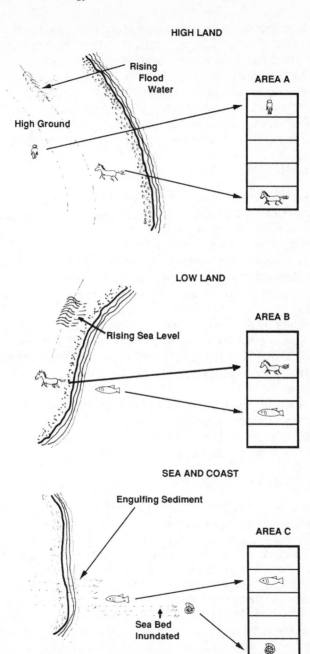

Fig. 2D How the geological fossil sequence could be produced
by animals all living at the same time.

In this scenario, the animals are swept in to the strata during different stages of the flood, and the particular sequence depended upon the local conditions as the waters engulfed various areas.

Thus, the broad sequence of fossils found in the strata does not chart the way in which they evolved, but the stages in which the various types were engulfed in the rising Flood waters. In the chaos that such an event would create, 'discordant' fossils found at levels that are not in an evolutionary sequence can easily be explained.

2. THE MISSING 'LINKS'

In some evolutionary charts, the main groups are linked with a dotted line, as shown in the frontispiece. Other charts omit such links entirely (which is the correct way they should be shown), whilst still others use a solid line between them. The problem facing the evolutionist is that virtually *no* fossils have been discovered which link these main groups. As it is crucial to the theory that they *must* have come from *some* earlier ancestor, using a dotted line effectively says — 'We think that mammals evolved from reptiles, but we have no proof'!

A writer might join them with a solid line, but he might then be challenged to provide the evidence of such links that he infers have been found. An example would be the many inadequate attempts to establish the fossils that would provide the link between reptiles and mammals.

On the other hand, if he draws it correctly, then there should be a distinct gap between the groups. But this would draw attention to the fact that the groups appear independent of previous types, and such evidence hardly supports the theory of evolution.

3. POLYSTRATE TREES

In several quarries around the world, as the face has been opened up, the fossilised trunks of trees have been exposed in a vertical position (Fig. 3). These trunks are often quite long and penetrate through many different layers. Geologists contend that the various strata were laid down at different times with periods of thousands or millions of years between the different layers. Yet if this were so, then a tree still upright when the lowest layer was deposited around it should have died and rotted away long before the top stratum was laid. Yet it can be seen that the trunk must have still been intact at this later stage. This is clear evidence that the deposits around the trunk were laid quickly before the trunk had time to decay. Such rapid deposition of the strata is far more in accordance with a Flood geology time scale than the slow sequence taking millions of years — the span of time so essential for evolution to take place.

a. Near Saint-Etienne (France)

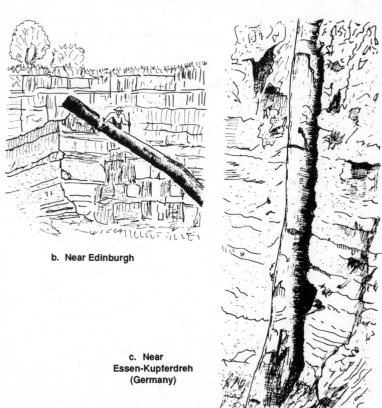

b. Near Edinburgh

**c. Near
Essen-Kupferdreh
(Germany)**

Fig. 3. Polystrate trees.

4. RATES OF DEPOSITION

In order to achieve as long a period as they can for the formation of the strata comprising the geological column, early efforts by Lyell and others attempted to show that, using the present known rates of deposition of certain strata, where there are great depths of this material it must have taken many thousands of years to have formed. This however is a far too simplistic method of examining such a complex subject.

One of the more modern exponents of this approach is Dan Wonderly who examines the subject in his book 'God's Time Records in Ancient Sediments' [2]. This book is often referred to by both long-age creationists and theistic evolutionists who do not accept that the earth is only a few thousand years old. It is noticeable that when the former are asked how long the earth has been in existence, they generally are unwilling or unable to give a figure.

Wonderly examines several strata, and tries to demonstrata how long it must have taken to lay them down. His reasoning, however, is very flawed, and I give one example to demonstrate this.

He takes the whole of chapter 3 to examine the slow growth of coral in the Pacific. He describes at great length the careful measurements by one researcher of the deposition of fossilised coral on living coral reefs which is about 8mm per year. He then quotes the very deep drillings on the islands of Bikini and Eniwetok. The drillings at the latter are quoted as going 'through 4,610 ft of reef deposit before striking the volcanic rock (basalt) base' [2p33]

He continues,

'It is of course true that no one is able to determine the exact length of time which was required for growing such an extensive reef, but it is obvious that it is a very long process. If we divide the thickness of the Eniwetok reef by Mayor's 8mm of deposit per year, we arrive at 176,000 years of continuous growth required for the laying down of this much thickness. However, this would be a false picture, because of the many factors which retard the build up of the reef, as discussed above. Thus the total length of the time required for forming the 4,600 foot reef deposit of Eniwetok was undoubtebly many times the 176,000 years.' [2p33]

On the basis of his information, there would certainly seem to be a case for the lengthy deposition of reefs which would be far in excess of the 10,000 years maximum time scale acceptable to most young-age creationists. He presents a picture of an unbroken sequence of fossilised coral that has built up over thousands of years. One point that immediately arises is to question the assumption that environmental conditions would have been so constant for such a

long period of time. This is only a minor quibble however, for one
has only to turn forward two pages, to find that he completely
demolishes his own arguments.

On page 35 he gives a description of what was actually brought
up in the drillings on this island, which I quote.

> 'We can not, in this volume, give a detailed description of the local
> stratigraphic column which was elucidated by the Eniwetok
> drillings, but a brief description of what the drilling cores revealed
> will help explain why we must regard the atoll as having a long
> history ... *of course practically all of it is limestone, with many
> fossils — especially corals, foraminifera and algae — embedded
> in it.* Numerous, and sometimes extensive, sections of the column
> were composed of hard, fossilised, cemented coral skeletons.
> Other sections were sometimes composed of limy *debris* which
> contained high percentages of the skeletons of other types of
> calcium secreting organisms' [2p35].

Contradicting the picture he had previously painted, the
drillings were not through a uniform material of fossilised coral that
had grown in place, but through a mass of limestone in which were
embedded some coral and other calcium-secreting organisms. The
great depth of material would appear to be a deposition of limestone
that swept up numerous organisms, sometimes in whole blocks,
under what seem to be catastrophic conditions.

To divide this great depth of mixed material by the 8mm
measured rate of present day coral fossils to obtain the total time of
growth is such a gross error that it completely undermines the whole
point of the book. Other errors could also be given. Yet this book is
still quoted approvingly by some. How they could have missed this
most obvious flaw, when the evidence is clearly set before them, is
perhaps a matter worth pondering on.

His arguments for other examples of slow deposition are also
incorrect, and his conclusions regarding the time taken for the
limestone deposits in the Grand Canyon have also been criticised
[3]. It is upon this erroneous interpetation of the evidence, however,
that he then proceeds to build a very inadequate case for special
creation over a long period of time, with his explanation of the
Genesis account having to conform to this scenario.

Recent sedimentation experiments

A number of sedimentation experiments have recently been carried
out which have given some surprising results. Numerous thin layers
of different (coloured) grain sizes can appear under conditions of

rapid deposition. This refutes the uniformitarian assumption that these must have been laid down slowly under very calm conditions. These results could have a bearing on the interpretation of how the different layers of the geological strata were formed. If this is so, then much radical rethinking may be needed on the whole subject by both creationists and evolutionists. I have given a brief summary of the experimental results in section III D 2 under 'Varves'.

B. FOSSIL DATING OF STRATA

The geological chart is often claimed to provide conclusive proof of evolution, for (in general) the more highly evolved and 'modern' animals appear later in the strata than 'simpler' extinct types. But there is a most serious objection to this inference which completely undermines any claim that the strata demonstrate evolutionary progress. This is that the strata were first classified, named and positioned on the chart on the assumption that, over vast periods of time, many species had failed to survive in 'the struggle for life' and had in time become extinct.

In his three volume work 'Principles of Geology', published in the 1830's, Charles Lyell laid the foundation for the classification of many of the geological strata as they are taught today. Some of the strata he sorted out into a sequence such that those with a high percentage of fossils that were of a species that were still living were put at the top of the column, and those with few surviving species were put at the bottom. This sounds a reasonable assumption, but it implies that more and more species changed into others over a period of time. Thus, once again we can see that the whole chart is based upon the supposition that evolution has taken place. To claim now that it 'proves' evolution is simply to prove what you have already assumed.

Circular reasoning.

A geologist, when he examines a rock, often wants to know to what age it belongs. He first of all lists the fossils it contains, and then consults various reference books which gives specific fossils (these are the 'index' fossils) that appear in particular strata. From the list of fossils in his rock, he finds the reference strata that has the greatest number of fossils that match his list, and from this he can determine the name (and the accepted age) of the strata with which he is dealing.

But it must be asked, where do the experts who wrote the book get their information from about the 'index' fossils? The answer is that they base their information upon the fossils that have been agreed as classifying the strata in the first place. The whole process is simply circular reasoning, for the fossils, (already arranged in an evolutionary sequence) are used to classify the strata, whilst the strata are classified by the fossils they contain.

It is accepted that, broadly speaking, the chart is correct in showing the main sequence in the strata in which the different species groups appear, i.e. the first fossils of fishes usually occur in deeper strata than those of mammals etc. However, there are numerous fossils and other discoveries that contradict the evolutionary theory that is behind the column. The 'Flood Geology' model mentioned above is not only a far simpler explanation of the sequence of the strata, but can also explain why there are so many fossils found that are 'contradictory' or 'out of sequence'.

C. PRECAMBRIAN STRATA

In the examination of great depths of Precambrian strata, small spheres and markings have been claimed as evidence of cells which later evolved into complex organisms. There have also been discovered what are said to be fossils of filamentous bacteria, and layered bands called 'stromatolites' that are mounds built by microbial communities such as algae.

The problem of the atmosphere

One of the many obstacles facing the evolutionists is to give even a reasonable explanation of how the first living organism came into existence. We will be considering later the importance of amino acids in living tissues, but suffice it to say that they cannot be formed chemically in our present atmosphere due to the large amount of oxygen which would immediately destroy them. It is therefore postulated that the atmosphere of the early earth was reducing (without oxygen). Anaerobic bacteria exist today that can function in such an atmosphere, and it is therefore said that these evolved first. Later, as oxygen became available, normal photosynthesis and oxygen-using (aerobic) metabolisms developed.

Such a scenario is, however, pure speculation and there is no scientific evidence for it. It *has* to be promoted in order to explain how amino acid chains that make proteins could have formed in the first place.

1. ARE THEY FOSSILISED CELLS?

The question must be asked whether these small marks and patterns really are fossilised forms of early life, for there is still considerable doubt about such evidence. One researcher acknowledged that ' ... apart from algae and a few faint traces of other forms, the Precambrian strata have yielded almost no fossils and have offered no clues to the origin of their Cambrian invertebrates.' [5] Indeed, some of these 'cells' have later been found to be inclusions of natural material within small voids that look like cells! [6].

One of the most revealing examinations of Precambrian fossils was reported in Bulletin 189 of the Geological Survey of Canada (1971) by H.J. Hofman. He entitled his paper 'Precambrian Fossils, Pseudofossils, and Problematica in Canada' and the general impression is that he seems to be dismissive of virtually all the fossils found in this period. In his abstract he said that macro-pseudofossils and micro-problematica 'make up the largest number of described forms'.

When the fossilised patterns, now called 'stromatolites', were first discovered they were virtually ignored as being just an unusual type of rock formation. Subsequently, when Darwin produced his theory, they were claimed to be fossil algae, and a furious debate ensued. Interestingly, Hofman declines to discuss the subject in detail, and it is possible that, as they are now so firmly entrenched in evolutionary dogma, to cast doubt upon their origin might affect his professional standing. Looking at the pictures he gives, they seem to be simply a series of layered patterns in the rock.

He reports that a similar debate arose about a type of patterning claimed to be biological in origin named Eozoon canadense. However, after much controversy, a vote of senior geologists was taken in 1864 (when the theory of evolution had not yet dominated academic thinking). Nine voted that it was not biological in origin and four voted that it was.

Hofman was able to produce a patterning very much like an 'Aspidella' fossil using oil and powder in the laboratory. He also gives a series of diagrams to show how a crack in mud could have had layers on either side compressed and curled over to form a hole that might be claimed to be evidence for the existence of life. Regarding the classification of the strata, he contends that several fossils said to be forms of life are not actually in the Precambrian strata, and should therefore be dismissed.

In his summary, Hofman suggests that there are only three areas, seemingly the contentious stromatolites, that may be biological in origin, and some of these are problematical also. He finally quotes another expert who said that most fossils described as biological in origin 'are those structures that exhibit a certain radial, cellular, or rhythmic pattern ... chemical and mechanical processes can imitate the architecture of organisms'.

It should be remembered that evolutionists *must* have evidence that life began as a simple collection of chemicals that gradually evolved into the complex living organisms existing today. It is therefore quite likely that these layered structures or minute markings in the Precambrian may have a perfectly natural explanation, but they have been pressed into use as 'evidence' of the early life badly needed as precursors of the phenomenal outburst of extremely complex fossils found in the Cambrian strata immediately above.

It is therefore suggested that this whole subject needs further investigation and clarification before being accepted as accurate.

2. THE EDIACARAN FOSSILS

There has been some publicity given to the discovery of animal fossils in Precambrian strata at Ediacara in South Australia [5]. Glaessner, in his description of the finds, expresses surprise regarding the similarity that some of the Precambrian fossils have to species still alive today.

He reports that jelly fish, soft corals, worms and some other strange animals, as well as fern-like plants, had been found in a layer 30m (100 ft) below the top of the Precambrian strata. Above that level there is Cambrian strata which seemingly is free of fossils for a further 150 m (500 ft), and it is only then that typical Cambrian fossils are found. Thus for some 180 m (600 ft) which on an evolutionary time scale might represent some millions of years, there is no evidence of any life whatsoever.

A catastrophic creationists explanation for this sequence would be that these small marine creatures were overwhelmed by the fossil-free material rising from the depths of the earth at the time of the Flood when the 'Fountains of the Deep' burst forth. How the evolutionist can explain a gap of millions of years when life seemingly ceased to exist in this area at least would be of interest, and Glaessner makes no attemp to do so. It appears to me that in publicising these finds, far from 'solving' the problem of the lack of Precambrian fossils, they present more problems to the evolutionists than they do to the creationists.

Interestingly, Stephen Jay Gould has criticised the claim that these fossils are very similar to those of the Cambrian [7] for he says that there are several fundamental differences between them. He suggests that the Ediacaran fossils were 'a unique and extinct experiment in the basic construction of living things. Our planet's first fauna was replaced after a mass extinction, not simply improved and expanded.'

This is a strange conclusion to reach. Without saying it, he seems to accept that there was not *one* period during which cells evolved and developed into multicellular sea creatures but *two*. Are we to believe that the miracle of the emergence of the first living and self-reproducing cells that combined to form distinct organisms occured twice on this planet? In this article he concentrates on an apparent 26 million year cycle of large scale extinctions in the geological column. He seems to have overlooked the implications of what he claims was a first total extinction of all known life.

A wrong classification?

The discovery of fossils in what is labelled Precambrian does also raise the question of circular reasoning considered above. Fossils are used to date and label the various strata. Broadly speaking, where there are no fossils in deep strata, it is classed as Precambrian. But here we have fossils in a deep strata, and some of the fossils are similar to those in upper layers. Strictly speaking, should it be called 'Precambrian', or is it more like one of the many 'displaced' strata that abound in geology? Had this strata with these fossils been found at a different level between strata with which it conforms, it would probably have gone unnoticed as being unremarkable.

That the experts have difficulty in knowing precisely where the Precambrian ends and where the Cambrian starts was aknowledged in 1983 when an international committee failed to agree on how this could be defined. No less than seven criteria were proposed and none accepted [8]. This gives some idea of the problem that defining these strata presents even to the experts. This uncertainty also allows the gradation of various fossils so that using a certain sequence, the gradual emergence of complex organisms could be given some support. It is this wrong classification of some strata as Precambrian that Hofman criticised in his Bulletin.

What is certain is that all the simple structures found in the Precambrian strata, apart from the unique Ediacaran, even if it were proven that they were biogenic, can in no way be claimed as being adequate precursors of the vast numbers of very complex and perfect organisms which lie immediately above them in the Cambrian stratum.

3. POLLEN GRAINS.

Pollen grains are minute cells that can be very resistant to weather conditions. They also have a distinctive shape, such that the pollen of each plant can be identified. In view of their comparative abundance, small size that allows them to lodge in obscure places and their resistance to destruction, they are useful in identification and correlation of various materials. They can be of use in checking the location ascribed to an article and upon datings etc. and the whole subject has grown rapidly in recent years. For example the method was used in the examination of the Turin Shroud by collecting the types of pollen found within its cloth, and seeing if they correponded to plants known to exist in the area of Palestine.

Clifford Burdick discovered pollen grains in upper layers of the Precambrian at the bottom of the Grand Canyon in America [9]. Some of the pollen matched those of present day flowering plants, but as it contradicted standard evolutionary thinking he was strongly challenged. Since then, many finds of pollen in Cambrian and Precambrian strata have been made which completely upsets the accepted stages of evolution for plant life [10].

Although contradicting evolution, they can nevertheless be explained by the Catastrophist's scenario, for clearly the early strata labelled Cambrian and the upper layers of the Precambrian were laid down at a time when modern plants and others that were to become extinct were already flourishing. This is a feature that would have to be built into any creationists interpretation of how the strata were laid down.

D. CAMBRIAN FOSSILS

We have examined the virtual absence of fossil forms in the Precambrian. This has always been a problem to the evolutionist who needs a nicely graded series in the strata from single cells to multi-cell groups grading into more complex forms. This has not been found, however.

In the Cambrian stratum immediately above it, there suddenly appear large numbers of very complex forms of life such as trilobites, ammonites, belemnites and other similar small sea creatures known as invertebrates (i.e. without a backbone). Trilobites (Fig. 4) have scales, legs, and their compound eyes are just like those of flies. Yet they appear over the Precambrian which has no 'simple' or 'primitive' ancestors that the evolutionist would have liked to see. This surely speaks of the sudden creation of life.

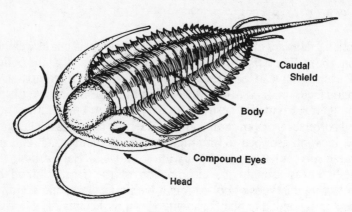

Fig. 4. A Cambrian Trilobite

In recent years there have been discovered some extremely unusual animals in Cambrian strata known as the Burgess Shales in Canada [5]. They display such a strange variety of forms, unlike any others known today, that it has surprised even the experts, and they have had great difficulty in classifying them. They vary in size, from about 1" (25mm) to 8" (200mm) long, and I illustrate some of them in Fig. 5. They are just another example of the amazing range of perfectly developed animals that suddenly appear in the Cambrian.

The Hallucigenia specimen was first drawn as illustrated in Fig. 5b, but closer examination showed that there were pairs of legs on the 'top' of the creature, which had been drawn upside down. Fig. 5e gives the latest version, whilst Fig. 5f shows another amazing creature found in Cambrian strata in China.

In order to 'explain away' the absence of precursors of these complex organisms, evolutionists have claimed that these early fossils were destroyed by the intense heat and extensive pressure which acted upon these deep strata.

But there are great depths of the Precambrian which consist of clays and other strata that are well able to preserve fossils yet do not have any. Other explanations attempting to overcome this problem have been shown to be equally unsatisfactory.

E. NO EVIDENCE OF PLANT EVOLUTION

If the theory of evolution is correct then one would expect to see much reference to the evolution of plants in the various books. Yet when they are consulted, the very small amount of space devoted to the evolution of plant life is very noticeable. Examination of several

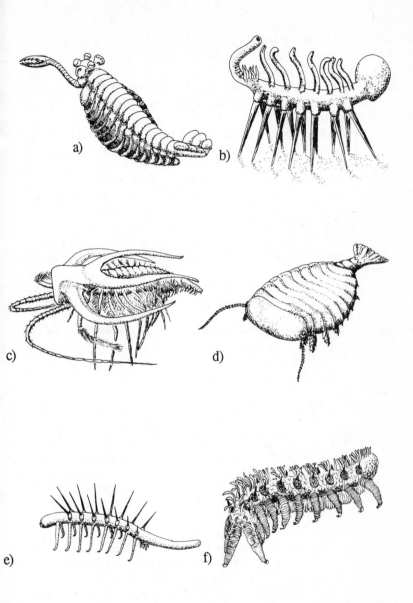

Fig. 5. Some strange animals in Cambrian strata —
(not to the same scale)
a) Opabinia b) Hallucigenia (first version) c) Marrella
d) Sineyia e) Hallucigenia (second version)
f) A creature found in China

books has shown that usually little more than one paragraph is devoted to the subject, and even then it consists mainly of a description of present-day plants and their classification, the evidence for their evolution being hardly referred to. In one book the evolution diagram has a question mark on all the dotted lines linking the different groups, whilst on another there are no joining lines given at all, from which one could conclude that they were all created independently!

In what might be considered as one of the official publications of the Natural History Museum on the subject, the book called 'Evolution' [11] makes no reference to plant evolution in the text at all but gives some of the groups on the usual geological 'column'. Even then, the various groups are not joined by lines connecting them together. A later more popular publication entitled 'Origin of Species' [12] omits not only any chart of plant evolution but even the usual full geological column such as we have in the frontispiece. The more guarded way in which evolution is being presented to the public is noticeable.

It might be thought that the evidence is not available because fragile material such as wood and leaves have decayed quickly and/ or been destroyed during the laying down of the various rock strata. But this is not correct, for there is a considerable amount of fossilised plants in the geological layers. Indeed, all coal measures consist of nothing but compressed plants. The main problem facing the evolutionist is that the evidence these fossils give is very confusing.

One way that is sometimes used to 'grade' plants on the evolutionary scale is to determine what characteristics are 'advanced' and what are 'primitive'. But how do you determine what the 'advanced' features are as against those that are 'primitive'? One expert will give one list of items, but many of his items will be contradicted by another expert who will give a quite different list, simply because deciding what is primitive and what is advanced is a purely subjective activity. One would expect a primitive plant to die out due to the greater competition from its more 'advanced' neighbours. Yet we find that the common Buttercup, said by one expert to be primitive, is still successfully flourishing (as gardeners know well) compared to the 'advanced' Love-in-a-mist.

As far as the fossil evidence is concerned, we have already discussed the discovery of pollen grains in the Precambrian, and the problem this presents to the evolutionist. As well as pollen, there are numerous fossilised plants found in early strata that are identical to those found living today. So much so, that the existing ones are called 'living fossils'. This is not unlike the Coelocanth, once only known as a fossil fish, but now found to be still living.

There is one group of plants, the switch-ferns (Psilophytes), that appear in the Devonian period, but there is no other record of them at all until we reach the present day, for they are still living. Thus, 400 million years ago these plants developed and flourished, but then for 350 million years they somehow survived without leaving a trace of their presence in any of the strata!

Just as difficult for the evolutionist to explain is the persistence of algae. These are found in Cambrian rocks older than 600 million years and in all strata since then. They are said to be one of the most primitive forms of life, and that they probably gave rise to all plant life. Yet whilst they have had great competition from numerous forms of highly developed plants for millions of years, they have nevertheless persisted in their present form and have survived seemingly unchanged. Despite great environmental pressures, they have not found it necessary to evolve.

Indeed, evolutionists have difficulty in providing a sequence of progress of plant life that agrees with the fossil record. In a book entitled 'An Evolutionary Survey of the Plant Kingdom' [13] a chart is given on page 602 captioned 'Flow diagram of probable phylogenetic relationships among the main groups of plants'. This places the 'simple' forms such as viruses and bacteria at the bottom and branches upwards to the 'advanced' flowering plants at the top. This presents to the reader a tidy chart of the 'probable' progress of plant evolution. When the text is examined, however, and the earliest dated strata in which the various classes are found are plotted on this same chart, a quite different picture appears.

One would expect 'early' plants at the bottom of the chart to appear in older strata, laid down in say Cambrian to Silurian periods (570 — 408 Myrs ago). However, several do not appear in the fossil record until much later than they should do if they are supposed to be ancestral to other types. Lichens, for example, are not found until the Miocene (24 Myrs ago). Other 'early' plants that are found in later strata are Diatoms — Jurrasic (208 My) and Red Algae and Brown Algae — Triassic (245 Mys).

In the upper section of the chart, several plants appear in later strata than others they are supposed to give rise to.

With such problems in trying to trace the way in which plants evolved, it is little wonder that the subject is only briefly referred to in the popular textbooks.

Coal deposits

The theory of evolution has some difficulty in providing an adequate explanation of how these beds of plant remains could have been deposited one above the other for many layers. Usually it is proposed that the bottom layer certainly grew in the position that it is found, as often there is a 'seat earth' around a few roots in the lowest strata. Other layers above may have been grown in the area or alternatively transported to it from another place.

Generally it is thought that the forest gradually subsided and was then covered with sediments under the water, and then rose up again above the water, allowing another forest to develop. This was in turn submerged and covered, only to rise up allowing further growth. Thus, in order to produce the many layers that there are in most coalfields, it is necessary to have the land rising and falling by just the right amount some 10 - 50 times — rather like a Yo-yo!

Another claim made is that it takes millions of years for wood to be turned into coal. Recent experiments [14] have shown, however, that the application of intense heat and vibration (probably generated by earthquake activity) can strip the hydrogen atoms off the cellulose and convert it into pure carbon in a matter of minutes and even seconds! What may not also be realised is that the well-known black coal that fuels our fires appears to be the remains of types of trees that are quite different from the normal trees that we have today. These latter form the large deposits of brown coal that exist in many places.

Evolutionists have much difficulty when trying to explain the origin of coal, but there is now evidence of a sequence of events that may have operated during catastrophic flood conditions that supports the young-earth creationists scenario. This will be considered in the companion volume.

F. GAPS IN THE RECORD

When Darwin wrote his 'Origin of Species' he admitted that the geological evidence was very much against his theory, but he claimed that this was due to the 'imperfect nature' of the fossils that had been discovered up to that time. He felt sure that with enough searching of the rocks there would be a complete range of fossils that would show the progress of evolution from one species to another. Over one hundred years later these fossils are still lacking. Although new fossils are being discovered, they consistently find many fossils of the same species, but none of the intermediate types that the theory so badly needs. It is this continued obstinacy of the geological evidence in failing to produce the much-needed evidence that has forced paleontologists to reconsider their theories. The result has been the theory of 'Punctuated Equilibrium' that we will be discussing in section IF3 below.

When evolutionists are challenged to provide a sequence of fossils linking the major groups, one of the examples they often give is that of an unusual bird, known as Archaeopteryx, which they claim links birds with reptiles. Similarly, for a series of animals which demonstrate the evolution of one animal into that of a different sort, they refer to the evolution of the horse. Both these appear very frequently in textbooks about evolution and the evidence seems to be convincing ... until it is closely examined.

1) ARCHAEOPTERYX

This is a bird about the size of a pigeon that was found in the Upper Jurassic stratum. There are two main specimens, both found in Germany. One was found in 1861 and now resides in the British Museum. The other was found in 1877 and is held in the Berlin Museum, and as this is the better specimen it is the one illustrated in Fig. 5.

The very soft fine clay into which Archeopteryx had fallen had hardened and preserved the very fine detail of its form. Close examination showed that it had some unusual features. It had small teeth in its beak, a hook halfway along the leading edge of its wing, thin ribs like a lizard and a long bony tail with feathers. As reptiles have features similar to these, it has been described as 'a feathered dinosaur'. The discovery of this bird was hailed as evidence that birds had evolved from reptiles, and that the scales of reptiles had gradually become feathers which eventually enabled them to fly.

Could this have been the case? It is hardly likely. There are five main aspects that refute this proposal.

I) UNUSUAL FOSSILS FREQUENTLY DISCOVERED.

It must be remembered that there are fossils of many strange creatures that do not exist today. There is an enormous variety of fossilised animals, and this specimen is much less peculiar than many that have been discovered. It has a few unusual features that reptiles have also, but it is far from being a reptile as such. There are many strange features in animals and birds both living and fossilised. For example, even today, the young Hoatzin bird in South America and the young ostrich have a hook on their wings similar to that of Archaeopteryx. Also, later fossils of birds have been found with teeth like Archeopteryx.

II) EMBRYONIC ORIGIN OF FEATHERS.

There is one damaging fact that proves that it is impossible for a reptile's scale to have ever become modified over many years into a feather. In the embryonic stages, the feather of a bird develops from a completely different part of the embryo to that from which the scale of the reptile arises. The scale could not therefore have gradually 'frayed at the edges' to become a feather, for the latter was created with its own special features and origin within the germ cell. The 'frayed scales' scenario is but one more example of superficial wishful thinking by the writers of books on evolution for popular consumption, who have failed to delve deep enough into the subject.

[There is an interesting event that is directly linked to the pursuit of evidence for the evolution of the feather. As part of Scott's last expedition to the South Pole in 1912, Dr. Wilson, 'Birdie' Bowers and Apsley Cherry-Garrard went to the breeding ground of the Emperor penguins during the bitterly cold depth of the winter period to obtain their eggs. Fully convinced by the recapitulation theory and that birds evolved from reptiles, the scientists expected eggs from these 'primitive' birds to show how feathers develop in the embryo of a predecessor of true birds. When dissected, however, it was found that the development of feathers was quite distinct from that of scales even in the very early stages of the embryo, and therefore no link could be established [15p315]. The fascinating account of how these three brave men almost perished during 'the worst journey in the world' on what was called 'the weirdest bird nesting expedition ever' can be read in Cherry-Garrard's book [15]. It is thought-provoking that this dangerous mission should have been so willingly undertaken to prove a point in a popular and accepted theory that is nevertheless fallacious.]

III) NO SCALE-TO-FEATHER TRANSITIONS.

It is important to note that no creature, fossilised or living, has ever been discovered which has scales that are half way to developing into feathers. A feather is an extremely complicated piece of equipment. If you look at a feather under a powerful microscope, you will see between the finest of the branches (barbs) a series of 'hooks and eyes' called barbules (see Fig. 7A). These can be linked together not unlike the 'Velcron' used in place of buttons on windcheaters, etc. These hooks are minute, and there can be over a million of them on one feather alone. It would have taken an enormous span of time for such a complex piece of equipment to have evolved by chance, and there should be many half developed fossilised stages. Yet in all the searching of the rocks, never has anything like a half evolved feather ever been found — and I am confident that it never will.

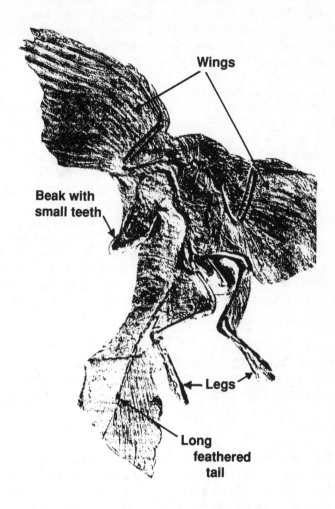

Fig. 6. Archeopteryx — The Berlin specimen.

It is clear from the impressions of the feathers of Archaeopteryx that they were used for flying, for the shaft (rachis) is not in the centre of the feather. This means that the feather will want to twist with the air pressure on one side. On the up beat, the feathers twist and the wing is opened up slightly and the air can pass through easily [Fig. 7B]. On the down beat, each feather is restrained by the ajacent one, and the wing is virtually air tight.

In addition, the long feathers (primaries) on the tips of the wings can be opened up for efficient flying. The difference in pressure between the lower and upper surfaces creates a vortex at the ends of the wings [Fig. 7B]. There is less turbulence from a series of small thin 'wings' (i.e. one individual feather) than there is from one large wing — such as many hawks have — which is therefore the more efficient design.

IV) HALF WAY STAGE IS NOT VIABLE

Have you ever thought how a reptile that was half way to becoming a bird could possibly function efficiently during the transition period? Imagine a reptile in such a situation. It has very long feather-like fronds spreading from its forelimbs, its rear legs are getting thinner and it is half way to walking or hopping on them like a bird. The fronds are not developed enough to enable it to fly or even glide, but are an encumbrance to it as it tries to move along the ground. Indeed, as it cannot crawl properly and cannot fly, it would be easy prey for a predator, who would make short shrift of that particular development — thereby wiping out this newly evolving species. Quite simply, an animal half way between a reptile and a bird could not survive and would soon be eliminated. Archeopteryx is certainly an unusual but perfectly designed bird and does not form a link with reptiles.

V) EARLIER BIRDS FOUND.

Finally, the fossilised remains of two birds have been found in strata some 75 million years older than the dating for Archaeopteryx. [16] It would seem that Archeopteryx has been knocked off its perch!

Is it a fake?

In 1983 a letter appeared in the Creation Research Societies Quarterly by M. Trop pointing out that in the British Museum specimen there was a discrepancy between the main slab (which has the bones and feather features clearly visible) and the counterslab (which surprisingly has far fewer features visible). He noticed that there was a small lump on the main slab that had no corresponding depression on the counterslab. This eventually gave rise to a detailed investigation by a number of experts who published their results. They claimed that they had proof that the fossil was of a small dinosaur to which had been added imprints of feathers by forgers in Germany where two examples had been discovered. As the subject is worthy of further examination, I have given a brief overview of the controversial claims and defences in Appendix 1.

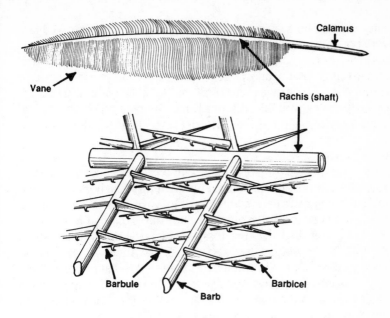

Fig. 7A. A magnified view of part of a feather

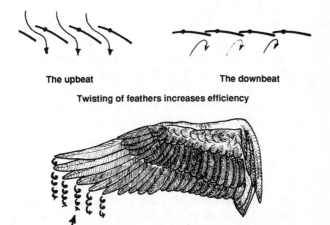

Fig. 7B. The operation of a flight feather.

Fig. 7. The flight feathers of a bird.

2) HORSE EVOLUTION

The series of horses showing how the modern horse evolved is a very popular subject in books about evolution. The gradual development from a small, multi-toed animal to the horse of today which effectively runs on one large 'finger' is displayed as a classic example of one species changing into another with all the intermediate stages available. A typical chart giving this is shown in Fig. 8 and we will examine this to point out several flaws in the evidence.

I) TIME SPAN.

One of the most glaring problems with this chart concerns the time span, and one does not have to know anything about horse evolution to realise that there is something seriously wrong with such charts. If you examine the full geological chart shown in the Frontispiece, it can be seen that the first fossil mammal appears in the strata roughly 200 million years ago. Since that time, all the known animals throughout the whole world are said to have evolved into the thousands of species we have today. In Fig. 8, the chart, which deals only with the upper five strata, shows that horses started to develop into the modern horse about 60 million years ago, the main feature being the enlarging of one 'finger' and the loss of the others. Yet, if you stop and think, surely there is something wrong with the time taken for this small change.

If it took 200 million years to evolve *all* known animals, then it should have taken only a minute fraction of that time simply to modify a horse's hoof! Yet it took roughly one third of this time (60 million years) according to these charts. The ratio between these two developments should not be a factor of three but many thousands. This glaring anomaly greatly discredits the whole chart and the question therefore arises — how was it composed in the first place? The answer is simple.

II) SELECTION OF THE EVIDENCE.

In all, some 250 horse-like fossils were found on the North American continent. From such a large range available, various fossils have been selected and arranged in a series in order to 'demonstrate' how the horse's hoof developed. But this series ignores both the time taken and in some cases the correct order of the fossils. There are so many similar species to choose from that each expert has chosen a different sequence of animals that show how the horse developed — and they cannot all be correct! Indeed, Dewar has said that he has seen no less than 20 such charts, and they were all different [17p90]!

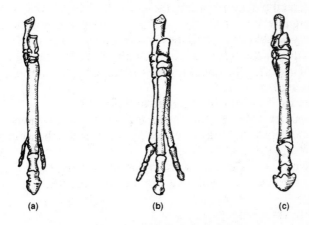

MYr	AGE	NAME	FORE FOOT	No. Toes	HIND FOOT	No. Toes	Lmb Vert	Ribs
	RECENT	Equus					6	17-18
	PLEISTOCENE			1		1		
5	PLIOCENE	Pliohippus						19
	MIOCENE	Merychippus		3		3		
	OLIGOCENE	Mesohippus		3				
37	EOCENE	Orohippus				3	8	15
				4				
58		Eohippus					6-7	18

A. A TYPICAL CHART OF THE "EVOLUTION" OF THE HORSE

B. THE HIND FEET OF (a) Eohippus
(b) Merychippus
(c) Equus

Fig. 8. The 'evolution' of the horse

Close examination of the various animals that appear in the sequence has shown that similar looking species were used to form the sequence which concentrated only on the different hoofs.

This is supported by the evidence given on the right hand side of the chart as this lists the number of Lumbar vertebrae (the vertebrae in the small of the back) and the number of ribs. The variations are large and yet are never referred to in these 'horse' charts. Thus while attention has been directed at the fore and hind limbs, as these are said to support evolution, the ribs and backbone are changing between each species and completely contradicting the theory. This strongly suggests that similar looking fossils that were actually different species have been used to form a series that is quite artificial. Other members of the series sometimes appear to be the same species with only minor differences between them.

III) THE GREAT LEAP.

There is one other point about the sequence. This fossil evidence was obtained from strata in America and leads up to the modern horse. But the earliest dated fossil horse was found in Europe. How it appeared there is a mystery, and attempts to create a similar sequence from European fossils have been unconvincing.

IV) THE PURPOSE OF THE 'VESTIGIAL TOES'.

The presented picture regarding these smaller bones is that as they became redundant for the purpose of the evolving horses, they effectively wasted away until they completely disappeared. This is not the true situation, for far from being useless they performed a variety of important functions in each particular horse. The bones—

a) strengthen the leg,

b) are used for attaching certain muscles, and

c) together with the canon bone, form a groove in which lies a ligament that supports the fetlock and counteracts the weight on the foot. [18]

As with the features of so many animals, what evolutionists class as vestigial actually have a vital function to play.

V) SOME CRITICAL COMMENTS.

It is interesting to see how evolution experts have rated this series as providing good evidence of the development of the horse. Prof. Kerkut, who teaches biology at Southampton University wrote an interesting book entitled 'Implications of Evolution' [19]. He is a convinced evolutionist, but without actually saying that the sequence of fossils of horse evolution is false, he quietly disparages it as being a satisfactory scientific explanation. This can be seen from some of his comments.

> [He refers to the increasing complexity of the horse evolution series as more fossils were discovered and says] 'In fact one could easily discuss the evolution of the story of the evolution of the horse.'
>
> 'At present, however, it is a matter of faith that the textbook pictures are true, or even that they are the best representation of the truth that is available to us at the present time.'
>
> [He suggests that horse evolution may be as chaotic as that of elephants where] ' ... every subordinate grouping is assumed to have sprung, quite separately and without any known intermediate stage, from hypothetical common ancestors in the Early Eocene or Late Cretaceous.'

Prof. Gaylord Simpson of Harvard University was a great populariser of evolution, but when he was writing for his professional colleagues he was much more cautious in what he claimed. He wrote:

> 'The continous transformation of Hyracotherium [an early fossil horse] into Equus, so dear to the hearts of generations of textbook writers, never happened in nature.' [20p119].

Charles Deperet, a great French paleontologist said: 'The supposed pedigree of the Equidae is a deceitful delusion ... ' [21].

In conclusion, the arguments presented above are surely sufficient to warrant the removal of this misleading series of fossil 'horses' from our textbooks.

3) RECENT ADMISSIONS

Creationists have always maintained that these gaps in the fossil record exist and have never been closed and never will be, despite protestations by evolutionists to the contrary. Now at long last, some prominent experts are admitting that this is correct, but have used this evidence to propose a third version of evolution called 'punctuated equilibrium' which we will consider presently. The two men who proposed this new idea are Prof. Stephen Jay Gould of Harvard University and Dr. Niles Eldredge. On November 21st 1978, The Guardian newspaper reported a lecture that Eldredge gave to the American Museum of Natural History. In this he is reported as saying:

> ' ... the smooth transition from one form of life to another which is implied in the theory is not borne out by the facts. The search for "missing links" between various living creatures, like humans and

apes, is probably fruitless, because they never existed as distinct transitional forms.'

'... no one has ever yet found any evidence of such transitional creatures.'

'... geologists have found rock layers of all divisions of the last 500 million years and no transitional forms were contained in them. If it is not the fossil record which is incomplete then it must be the theory'.

Here at long last is an evolutionist admitting what creationists have been saying for years. The Guardian correspondent, who headed the article 'Missing, believed non-existent', comments

'What is extraordinary is that in the last 120 years since Darwin appeared to have cracked the problem with elegant neatness in "The Origin of Species," the principle has withstood all attacks on it — and yet it still evolves loose ends.'

Punctuated equilibrium

On first reading this report, one might at first think that Eldredge was coming round to a creationist viewpoint. Unfortunately this is far from his and Gould's intention. They are the proposers of a new theory of the progress of evolution known as 'punctuated equilibrium'. This claims that all the species were continuing to live and breed with little change for many millions of years (equilibrium). Then suddenly, perhaps due to a change in the local climate or some similar severe ecological disturbance, the 'equilibrium' was 'punctuated' and new species suddenly arose as a result of these changes. These rapid developments are said to have occurred in small groups away from the main population, giving little chance of these intermediate fossils being found.

The main evidence produced is the gaps in the fossil sequences as we have noted. However, there is not a shred of genetic or other evidence which could possibly show how such new creatures could evolve very rapidly from normal parents. Admitting that these gaps existed, a theory known as 'hopeful monsters' was propounded in 1940 by Prof. Goldschmidt [22]. This suggested that quite suddenly a new species was produced from parents of a well established stock i.e. that a male and female reptile might produce a bird-like creature. As with punctuated equilibrium, no genetic explanation was given of how such an event could take place, and it was really a theory of despair in the face of the evidence of the gaps in the fossils.

It is perhaps an indication of the inadequacy of their case that evolutionists have to resort to such poorly substantiated theories as these. The production of this new theory is also an interesting illustration of a person's philosophy of life providing the basis of his 'scientific' theories. Prof. Gould is an admitted Marxist and the theory is a clear reflection of his ideology which on the political level claims that a revolution 'punctuates' a stable social system and thereby produces a new order of government. An evolutionist, Dr. Beverley Halstead, who was a geologist at Reading University, did not accept the new theory and pointed out that the British Natural History Museum is now publicising the theory. He noted that:

' ... a fundamentally Marxist view of the history of life will have been incorporated into a key element of the educational system of this country. Marxism will be able to call upon the scientific laws of history in its support, with a confidence that it has [not?] previously enjoyed' [23]

Cladograms

As a result of acknowledging that there are unbridgeable gaps in the fossil record, the idea of a gradual transition from one species to another has had to be reconsidered, and this has been reflected in the way that links between them are shown in diagrams. Where before fossils were placed in a line of supposed *sequential* evolution from say ape to man, they are now presented in cladogram charts as *relationships* to each other, as illustrated in Fig. 9.

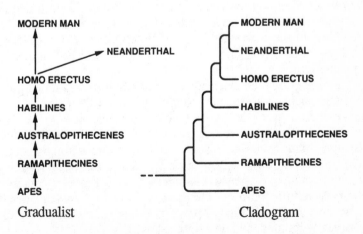

Fig. 9. The old 'Gradualist's' 'sequential' and new cladogram 'relationship' diagrams.

What is particularly significant is that no fossil is claimed to be the ancestor of any living species, only that it has a 'relationship' to them. Who man's ancestors really were is completely ignored, but that he DID evolve from some common ancestor is still firmly insisted upon by the linking lines to the left.

Cladists have met considerable opposition from conservative evolutionists, who are sometimes referred to as 'gradualists' as they contend that evolution progressed by a series of numerous small changes. The reason for this opposition is that cladism is a return to pre-Darwinian concepts — that there are no sequential links between any of the various species.

These diagrams are far more vague in the information they give than the older method, but this gives them one particular advantage. Any change in the relationships between the species can usually be accomodated by the redrawing of a few lines on the left hand side. This is far less likely to be noticed by the public than having to embarrasingly change the actual positions of the fossils on the diagram as frequently happened with the older system.

G. DISCORDANT EVIDENCE — AND THE ESTABLISHMENT

The geological chart in the Frontispiece is based upon the fossils in the various strata, the date applied to them and the sequence in which they are found. Man only appears on these charts in the last two or three million years. Therefore it would be quite contrary to the theory of evolution if evidence of human existence were found in say Cambrian or Cretaceous strata. If this were established, the credibility of the chart would be completely destroyed. Similarly, the discovery of say a horse in Devonian strata would have the same repercussions.

A number of such discoveries are reported in creationist publications, such as one devoted to this subject by Dr. Erick A. von Fange of Ann Arbor, Michigan entitled 'Time Upside Down'. An article in the Creation Science Quarterly for March 1991 (v27 n4) also gives many examples of stone implements found in early strata. With objects so obviously of human manufacture found with a degree of regularity, many will wonder why they do not appear more often in scientific journals. If they are reported they are considered to be 'puzzling' and quietly forgotten. Usually, however, they are completely ignored, and we might ask why?

The answer is quite simply that editors are reluctant to publish anything which contradicts evolution unless it has been personally discovered by an accredited scientist. Even if one does make such a discovery, he will be very cautious in what he says for he will be very aware of the implications. When such evidence, say a discovery in a coal seam, is reported by miners, it may receive some attention in a local newspaper but it will probably be dismissed as a 'fabrication', a 'practical joke' or something similar by the experts. The object will then be forgotten and lost unless a creationist makes enquiries and locates the object or obtains a signed statement about the discovery. He may not hear of the find until a long time afterwards, when much of the evidence that would have established its credibility may have been destroyed. When it is eventually published in a creationist magazine it will still be ignored by the scientists and dismissed as creationist propaganda. Thus, scientific respectability ensures that only the evidence supporting evolution receives wide coverage.

As scientific editors usually refuse to publish discoveries such as these unless found by an acknowledged expert, they can always thereafter be dismissed on the basis that 'no report has appeared in a reputable journal.' Thus evidence that supports the creationist viewpoint is caught in the circular reasoning of a 'catch 22' situation

— It is unacceptable as evidence (as evidence against evolution is not published in reputable journals)
— It will therefore not be published.
— As it has not been published in a reputable journal, it is unacceptable as evidence!

If any academic institution is approached to give an 'unbiassed' report on any discordant material, their usual attitude is to ignore it. If they are pressed to reply, they will invariably be dismissive.

What they cannot give is any assessement supportive of the creationist position. It takes little imagination to see that such a report would raise a storm for both the authors and the organisation involved. The position of the whole establishment would be questioned by those who control their committees or provide their funds. In view of this, it is hardly likely that the supervising authorities would allow anything to emerge that gave the creationist any credibilty whatsoever.

I would therefore suggest that there is virtually no likelihood of any established authority providing evidence that could be damaging to evolution theory. To approach them in the hope that they will provide an 'independant' and subjective viewpoint on any contentious issue is surely wishful thinking. The authorities involved are far too conscious that the whole future and reputation of their particular establishment is at stake, compared with which, providing an objective scientific report to a few troublesome creationists pales into insignificance.

H. GEOGRAPHICAL DISPERSAL OF ANIMALS

This is a subject that is rarely considered in any depth by both the evolutionist or the creationist, probably because neither has been able to present an adequate explanation for the almost idiosyncratic way in which many animals arrived in the very specific areas in which they are found.

There is much emphasis by evolutionists on the isolation of the Australian continent by what is called the 'Wallace' line, named after Alfred Russel Wallace the explorer and collector who was a friend of Darwin. This is the name given to the division between the very distinctive animals and plants on each side of a line that can be drawn between Australia and the Asian mainland. It is usually claimed that this line was crossed by the 'earlier' marsupials when there was a land bridge still existing. A channel is then thought to have opened up in the Mesozoic era before the 'later' placental mammals could follow them.

Similar isolation of species is recorded in many parts of the earth, where species are found in one special island or area and nowhere else. Another situation is where two identical (or almost identical) species are found on completely different continents with no seeming connection between them at all.

How did they arrive at these locations?

Evolutionists claim that the species evolved in one area, probably due to the rapidly changing ecological conditions, and then spread across the globe, but that they continue to exist only in particular areas where we find them now. This may sound reasonable, but the subject presents considerable problems when the fossil record is considered along with this distribution.

If a new species, (or genus or family that would eventually produce its particular type of species) evolved in one area, it is to be expected that as the members migrated slowly to various areas where feeding was available, then at least a few of them would be entombed in the strata and become fossilised. Thus the path of migration should be traceable in the strata to link with the present positions of known species. However it is found that there are very considerable discrepancies between the fossil record and the present locations of animals.

Some of the problems facing evolutionists in trying to explain the present disposition of animals are as follows;

i) Fossils of marsupials have been found in Australia, but none on the other side of the Wallace Line in Asia. Yet fossil marsupials have been found in Europe, North and South America and Africa. One would have expected at least some to be found nearer to the Australian continent than Europe.

In order to explain this, it has been suggested that instead of the two continents separating, they have comparatively recently come together. It is suggested that the Australian continent was joined to South America, where there are still marsupials, broke away from it and is now meeting the Asian continent. This would explain the large differences across the Wallace line. However, having solved this problem, another rises in its place, for if the marsupials were transported in this way, why were the placentals living with them not transported along with them also?

ii) If the Australian continent has been isolated for such a considerable length of time, it is strange that no other mammal-like Order has evolved during this period as happened on the mainland elsewhere. This indicates the stability of the species over very long periods of time.

iii) It is usually contended that having reached Australia, the 'inferior' marsupials were protected from the 'superior' placental animals by the separation of the continents. But this classification of 'inferior' and 'superior' is quite unwarranted.

It took several attemps to establish a rabbit population in Australia, which then grew prodigiously. Similar efforts with squirrels however failed. A few marsupials have crossed the Wallace line and are slowly spreading across Asia, despite competition from numerous placentals. Similarly, some placentals have crossed in the opposite direction and are sucessful in Australia. On the American continent, the marsupial opposum has comparatively recently spread into the North from the South, despite the competition of the 'better adapted' placental animals.

These examples are given to show that it is wrong to label one family or group as 'superior' to any other. The reason for a species spreading over an area is very complex, with a whole host of factors involved. These would include food supplies, disease, changes of environment etc., whilst for plants, the correct means of pollination must be available (i.e. particular flies might be needed in the area to be colonised.)

These points show that the evolutionist has considerable difficulty in providing an adequate explanation of the present dispersal of animals and plants.

For the creationist, the problem is not dissimilar, for an explanation is needed for why particular animals (or types) have reached certain areas after the Flood, and why other types are absent. Tentative answers to these difficulties will be examined in the later companion volume.

I. HUMAN 'MISSING LINKS'.

There is one subject in geology that has received more study and finance for expeditions and investigation than any other. This is the subject of the search for the links between the animals and man — the so-called 'missing links' of man's ancestry. A number of fossil fragments have been found at various times and places, each of them hailed with massive publicity as providing conclusive proof that man has descended from an ape-like ancestor.

An investigation of many of these discoveries, however, shows that most of them are little more than a few bone fragments, and that reconstructions or 'artist's impression' owe more to imagination than to scientific accuracy. I have criticised all the main fossil discoveries that are claimed to show that man has descended from apes in another book entitled 'Ape-Men — Fact or Fallacy?' [24]. I will therefore not go into the subject in any depth here but give an outline of some of the more famous fossils and the misleading claims that are made about them. There have, however, been some further revelations about the Piltdown hoax, and I have set these out in Appendix 2 for the readers interest.

1) JAVA MAN.

A Dutch medical doctor, Eugene Dubois, sailed to the Far East in 1887 determined to discover 'the first man'. He went to Java in 1891 where he found an ape-like skull cap and a year later on the same site but 14 metres (46 ft) away, he found a human upper leg bone (femur). He claimed that these bones were from the same individual who was therefore an upright, walking ape. He brought these and a few other bones back to Europe contending that they 'proved' that man was descended from apes. There was a great deal of controversy but with the amount of publicity surrounding the finds, more and more scientists accepted them as evidence of man's evolution. Dubois, however, locked the original fossils away and would allow no one to inspect them.

Thirty years later, in 1920, he shocked the scientific world by announcing that at the same time as he had discovered the Java 'man' fossils, he had also found two very human skulls on the island at Wadjak. The dating of the stratum in which they were found was roughly the same as for his Java 'man' but he kept their discovery secret for thirty years. He knew that if he had displayed all his discoveries, including the Wadjak skulls, he would never have succeeded in convincing the scientists that his leg and skull bones were of an ape-man.

His admission stunned the scientific world, but by then the skull and leg bone had been accepted as an important link in man's evolution, so his admission was virtually ignored.

As Dubois' evidence was so controversial, a full expedition was mounted to the same site on which he had found the original fossils, but they found no evidence whatsoever that confirmed his claims. Furthermore, in 1931 von Keonigswald was sent to obtain fresh evidence, but found only a few fossils, from which he 'reconstructed' a 'missing-link' skull.

2) PEKIN MAN.

Between 1926 and 1934 Teilhard de Chardin and Dr. Davidson Black carried out excavations at a site a few miles from Pekin and a number of fossil skulls were found. These were almost all in small fragments and a considerable amount of Plaster of Paris had to be used on them to obtain enough material to form a skull shape. On one of the reconstructions, a woman's face was modelled and named 'Nellie' — the result being given much publicity.

It was claimed that these were the skulls of ape-men. There was however a considerable amount of evidence that the site had been inhabited by human beings and that the skulls were only those of monkeys that they had caught and cooked for food. For example, there were thousands of pieces of quartz that had been the results of a stone tool making industry. There was also a 7 metre (24 ft) depth of ashes which could not possibly have been the work of ape-men.

In December 1929 there was an important announcement in the national press in England and America that ten skeletons had been found. Davidson Black considered them to be of a 'thinking being, standing erect'. Other well known experts made cautious comments on the importance of the finds, and a special announcement by Davidson Black on 29th December was eagerly awaited. However, no announcement was made and nothing more whatsoever has ever been said about these skeletons — it is as if they had never existed, for there has never been any further reference to them in the official journals.

What could have happened? I would suggest that close examination showed that they were far too human to be classed as ape-men, and the discovery of human beings on the site of the much publicised Pekin Ape-Man would have brought ridicule upon all the scientists who contributed to the work in any way. In view of this prospect, the whole subject was quietly hushed up, seemingly on an international level, for no questions have ever been raised by any learned body regarding the fate of these skeletons.

During the Second World War, all the specimens from the site were captured by the Japanese, and are said to be undiscovered to this day. Therefore a check on the accuracy of the reconstructions and a close examination of the actual bones is not now possible.

3) 1470 MAN.

This was à collection of fragments of skull pieces found by Richard Leakey in Kenya in 1972. The reconstruction however showed that it was a very human looking skull whilst a (second) dating test gave it an age of 2.6 million years. Leakey claimed that this human-like skull found in such early strata completely altered our ideas of man's evolution. However, over the next few years, he gradually changed his views so that this skull is now virtually ignored as it is so difficult to reconcile with the present views of man's ancestry. It is most likely a human skull as other human bones were found in the same strata, but the Natural History Museum's exhibition 'Man's Place in Evolution' gives only a picture of it and make no mention of what its position should be on man's family tree.

Several years after he had made the discovery, his mother, also an ape-man fossil hunter in Kenya, gave a lecture at the British Natural History Museum during which she said that Richard was reluctant to discuss 1470 Man, and was in fact wanting to 'kill off the habilines' (a group in which 1470 Man had been included). What was more interesting, however, was that at the end of the talk and after a series of flattering votes of thanks to the important speaker, the meeting was promptly closed. Seemingly the possiblity of embarrasing questions being asked from the floor was not welcomed.

4) EARLY HUMAN SKELETONS.

A number of human skulls and skeletons have been discovered in 'old' strata dated long before man is supposed to have appeared. Amongst them are the Castenedolo skull, the Calaveras skull, the Olmo jaw, the Galley Hill skeleton and several others [24p74f]. As they do not fit in to the evolutionary time scale of man's development, they are ignored or dismissed as burials or as hoaxes. Yet they were often found by reliable witnesses and the evidence is that they are genuine fossils from strata that are dated earlier than man is supposed to have appeared. It is only examination of old reports that has brought them to light, but they are still almost ignored today and when they are referred to it is usually to remove them as reliable evidence.

A typical example of the treatment that these fossils have received at the hands of experts ever since their discovery is provided by the Presidential Address given by E.T. Newton F.R.S. to the Geologists Association in 1897 entitled 'The evidence for the existence of man in the Tertiary period' [25]. All the fossils mentioned above that had been discovered at that time as well as many artefacts showing evidence of human workmanship were carefully considered. Despite much evidence which he provides, caution was advised on accepting them as their authenticity was 'not definitely proven'. Yet no satisfactory reasons for such conclusions were provided.

When dealing with the Java Man fossils of Dubois, the approach is quite different, for he eventually accepts that the fossils are of an ape ancestor of man. Although we know the skull and the human femur were 14m (46ft) apart, he glosses over this, saying 'although some distance apart ... there is little doubt that they belonged to the same individual.' [25p80]

Having accepted the authenticity of Dubois' (fabricated) Java ape-man, he then uses this to discredit the possiblity of true man existing in the earlier Tertiary times, for he says that that it is unlikely that true man could have preceded the Java ape-man.

Although couched in terms to appear an objective assessment of these fossils, it takes only a little careful examination of this paper to see the strong evolutionary bias behind the way in which they are denigrated. 'Java Ape-Man' had been discovered in 1892 and variously dated as Pliocene (Tertiary) by Dubois and Pleistocene by others. Therefore, the possibility of true man being contemporary or earlier would be strongly resisted by the proponents of the then still controversial theory of evolution. Java man was a lynch pin of the theory, for he formed the first evidence of a link between man and an ape ancestry.

Darwin had published his 'Origin of Species' in 1859, whilst this Presidential Address was given in 1897. There was therefore adequate time for the control of the major institutions in this country to fall into the hands of the comparatively small group of people that supported the theory of evolution. Once in control, they were determined to propagate the theory of evolution against the older and well-established Christian-based creationists [26p113].

5. 'HOMO ERECTUS'

This is the name given by evolutionists to a group of fossils that is claimed to be a distinct intermediate link between man and apes. It was first given to the two groups of fossils found at Java and Pekin. As we have seen, the first is really a human leg bone and a giant ape skull, whilst the second is a collection of ape skulls. Since then other fossils have been added to it to form the main group between homo sapiens (modern man) and all the ape classes.

Sometimes creationists refer to this group as though it is a valid species, but it must be remembered that it is has been deliberately fabricated by evolutionists to provide this most vital stepping-stone between us and our supposed evolutionary ancestors.

Homo erectus has never existed as a separate species but is a collection of portions of skulls and skeletons which the palaeoanthropologists (experts in fossil man) have put together to form this group. Where there is sufficient material of a skull or skelton, it can *always* be determined whether it is human or ape. Where only a small portion of say an ape has been found, then the 'human' features that it is said to possess are greatly exagerrated. If a slightly unusual human bone is found, its so-called 'ape-like' features will be emphasised. By putting a number of these doubtful fossils together, the classification of Homo erectus has been carefully fabricated over the years.

J. SUMMARY OF THE GEOLOGICAL EVIDENCE.

In this section we have criticised the composition of the standard geological column and the evolutionary assumptions which underlie it. Far from being convincing evidence for the theory, it can be seen that there exists much evidence against it, if one cares to examine the facts available in the more serious scientific periodicals or in well researched creationist literature.

It may well be asked what the creationist explanation is for the existence of the fossils if it is not evolution. Whilst there are different views on this, the one accepted by many is that the vast majority of the fossils and the strata they are found in were laid down at the time of Noah's Flood. This world wide cataclysmic disaster is more than sufficient to explain most of the geological deposits and their fossils. Indeed, the clear evidence of the catastrophic conditions under which the various strata were laid down is now accepted by a growing number of geologists.

It must be remembered that uniformitarian (evolutionary) geology has been taught at our universities for over 100 years. Against this background, creationists have the enormous task of a complete re-assessment of all the available evidence. As this evidence has been written entirely from a uniformitarian point of view it requires a complete reinterpretation of it from the viewpoint of catastrophism. Suffice it to say that the evidence is gradually being accumulated by the efforts of many creationist workers around the world and one or two models of the sequence of events that took place during that unique event are now under consideration and discussion.

One additional development is the possibility of a second period of catastrophic upheavals, which would explain many geological features. Where a period of quietness allowed a resurgance of life in some areas, this may have been subsequently destroyed by a local catastrophe as the long term geological effects of the Flood gradually decreased. This whole subject will be examined in the later companion volume on Genesis.

SECTION II — BIOLOGY

As Darwin frankly admitted, there was very little evidence that supported evolution in the geological strata. He therefore concentrated most of his attention on the enormous varieties of animals and plants that there are and collected together from various sources enough cases which he could cite as evidence that species can change from one to another. On quite inadequate evidence he blandly claimed that given sufficient time, all present forms could be achieved from earlier ancestors by natural processes.

In this section, the biological evidence often cited will be considered and then shown that far from supporting the theory, it is actually against it.

A. GENETICS

In the germ cells of animals (sperm and ovum) and plants (pollen) the information which determines the variety of the offspring is contained in a number of long complex molecules called chromosomes. Each has along its length millions of chemical groups called 'genes' which carry the coded information. Chromosomes in normal cells are in similar matching pairs but in the germ cells there is only one of the pair.

When the sperm unites with an ovum, the correct chromosome in each recombines with its pair and the full complement is made up. In this way, the offspring has some characteristics of the mother and some of the father. It is adequate for our purposes to consider that one gene determines a particular characteristic, but in actual fact, this simple idea is not the true situation. It has been found that certain characteristics are often determined by several genes and by complex interactions between them.

Most books on evolution deal with genetics at great length and show how it is a chance combination of dominant and recessive genes which determine various features in the offspring. When much space is devoted to an extensive explanation of the subject, complete with diagrams etc. the impression is given that irrefutable scientific evidence is being presented which supports the theory of evolution. A moment's careful thought however will show that really it is very much against the theory, for the characteristics of the offspring are already in the genes of the parents, and anything that the parents have learned during the course of their lives cannot be passed on to their offspring by means of their chromosomes. Indeed, the germ cells are formed in the embryo at a very early stage of its development, and it is therefore not possible to affect them during the adult life of the animal as a result of its experiences, as the chromosmes have already been produced.

Before going into the complex subject of genetics, it may be as well to define certain technical words used, for their appearance in books on evolution can cause much confusion. Whilst I have tried to avoid their use, understanding them will assist in following any discussion on the subject in other works.

A glossary of genetic terms

Alelles (or allelomorphs) — another name for the pairs of genes that modify the same characteristic, such as whether the eyes are blue or brown.

Diploid — the cell posseses the full number of paired chromosomes that are in normal cells. There are the same number of paired chromosomes before and after a normal cell division (mitosis).

Haploid — When the cell divides in a special way (meiosis) to form two germ cells ready for fertilisation, the number of chromosomes is halved, one of each pair going to a different germ cell.

Mitosis — the normal division of a cell to reproduce itself. The full number of paired chromosomes are retained in each cell.

Meiosis — the special division of a cell ready for fertilisation. Each of the resulting cells (gametes) has only one set of the pairs of chromosomes that are usually present in the normal cell.

Crossing over — At one stage in the formation of the germ cells, the pair of chromosomes split so that there are four of them. When the chromosomes are paired together, a small proportion of some of the genes cross over and change places with the corresponding but different gene opposite. This gives a very wide range of variations in the genetic code that results in the different features in the offspring.

Gamete — Sex cell carrying only one set (haploid) of the chromosomes.

Zygote — Cell resulting from the union of two germ cells (gametes) in which the normal number of paired chromosomes is re-established.

Homozygous — Genes appear at the same location on each of

the pair of chromosomes. There is often the possibility of two different forms of genes, usually one dominant and the other recessive, appearing at either location. When they are the same on each of the paired chromosomes then the cell is said to be homo- (the same)-zygous with respect to the particular feature, and the off-spring will have the variety of features (say shortness) that the gene controls.

Heterozygous — (hetero-different) Similar to homozygous, but in this case the genes on the pair of chromosomes are different. The offspring will then have the variety of features that are controlled by the more dominant gene (e.g. a brown-eye gene is dominant to a blue-eye gene).

Phenotype — The particular variety of a feature (e.g. tallness) shown by an offspring that has been created by its genetic makeup.

Genotype — The genetic constitution of an individual.

Gene pool — The range of the variations of characteristics that are available in the different genes that a species may possess. Dogs for example seem to have a very wide range of characteristics, which can be developed by selective inbreeding.

Genetic drift — When a cell divides into germ cells, each germ cell can only have one half of the available variations of the whole range of possible genes. Thus the gene pool has a reduced number of the varieties it could reproduce. If a small group of animals out of a large population breed together over several generations, they will show certain features more than others as compared to those of the variations in the larger population. Thus the genetic variability and features have 'drifted'.

It is sometimes claimed that a mutation or variation that may give as little as 1% 'advantage' over other members of a group could be significant in giving the organism a better chance of survival. Advantages of this order or even of 10%, however, would be completely swamped by the amount of change that is due to genetic drift. There is considerable resistance within a group against any significant changes in its genetic features.

Defining a species.

One of the many problems facing evolutionists is that of defining a species. The simplest and most usual means of determining a species is to say that it consists of those members who can interbreed and have viable offspring, and cannot interbreed with another group. This however is not adequate for a number of cases.

For example, species A may be fertile with species B & C but

B is not fertile with C. Which of them can then be claimed to be a distinct species? Whilst on this topic, it might be pertinent to ask Darwinists how they define a species. If all species are connected in an unbroken chain then no such thing as a distinct species would exist because all species would be connected. Indeed, how to define a species has never been finally agreed by biologists.

This inability to define a species also applies to creationists, and confusion can arise when dealing with the subject if it is examined in depth. As we have mentioned, Genesis states that animals reproduce 'after their kind', and Linnaeus began classifying animals to try to discover these limits of 'kinds', but no clear picture has emerged even today.

Those who specialise in classifying and defining species (taxonomists) face considerable problems in trying to agree on what will be classed as a species. As evolutionists prefer to see a gradual change of species over a time, some divide what are really variations into separate species. Those that tend to do this are known as 'splitters', as against 'lumpers', who usually encompass a range of variations as one species. Creationists are more interested in determining the basic 'kind' referred to in Genesis, and therefore would be looking not for a range that would be classed as a species but for groups of species that can be linked together to form one 'kind'.

The sort of group that might be one kind are say the 'dog' group, which would include dogs, wolves. foxes, jackals, coyotes and hyenas. Some creationists are examining the problems of how a kind could be defined and determined, so that that the present wide range of species can be collected into these major 'kinds' (baramin) referred to in Genesis.

1. MENDEL'S EXPERIMENTS REFUTE EVOLUTION.

Gregor Mendel was a monk who lived in Austria from 1822 to 1884. He had a degree in science and carried out experiments on plants to see if he could discover any relationship between the characteristics of the parents and those of the offspring. He found that they followed a simple law of proportion, the result in the offspring depending upon whether a particular feature was dominant or recessive. These simple laws apply to both plant and animal inheritance, for they both have the same basic method of cell division into germ cells and their reunification into one normal cell on fertilisation.

To give an example of how these laws work we can consider the case of a simple sort of human eye colouration. In humans, the gene for brown eyes is dominant whilst that for blue eyes is recessive (Fig' 10). In the paired genes, if both (or just one of them) are for brown eyes then the offspring will be brown eyed. If however both genes are for blue eyes (there being a 25% chance of this situation arising), then the offspring will be blue eyed. Recessive genes can be unknowingly transmitted through several generations, only becoming apparent when they are paired with another recessive gene, as can be seen in the third stage of Fig 10.

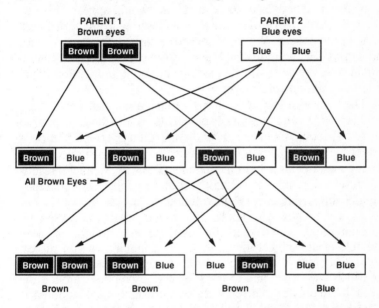

Note - the brown-eyed Parent 1 is shown as having two dominant "Brown-Eye" genes. They may, however have one dominant brown eye gene and one recessive blue eye gene. This would result in two chances of the four being blue eyed in the first generation.

Fig. 10. Mendel's theory of genetic inheritance.

There are two important factors as far as evolution is concerned.

Firstly, *all* the characteristics of the offspring are obviously in the genes of the parents to begin with. What happens is that the corresponding genes are 'randomly' paired up and the offspring's features are the combined result. Thus there is no way in which a totally new characteristic can appear in an offspring; it has to be present in the parents to begin with.

Secondly, there is no known way that a parent can possibly modify its genetic coding to include a particular new characteristic which has helped it to survive. In the higher animals (mammals etc.) the cells that produce all the germ cells throughout the life of the individual are separated out quite early in the embryonic stage. They are therefore unaffected by any normal activity of the animal.

Therefore, from these two considerations, it can be seen that all the varying features of any particular species were present in the very first parents. The wide variety of types is only a selection from a large choice of characteristics, usually described as a 'gene pool'. In the case of humans, as they spread over the earth, they would inbreed in certain areas and particular features such as dark skin of the negro or slant eyes of the chinese etc. would appear. It is this inbreeding in certain groups which provides us with all the different races we have today. We are all nevertheless still the same species and can easily intermarry and have fertile children. The different human races are due to local breeding variations and are nothing to do with evolution whatsoever.

The theory of evolution needs a genetic mechanism that can include a wide variety of totally new features into the gene pool so that they become fixed as part of the hereditary system. Mendel's results show that this is not the case, as the choice is limited to the genetic material already in the parents. The way Mendel's results are presented in most books however make people think that they actually support the theory of evolution.

As is well known, Mendel's results were published in 1866 but were not 'rediscovered' until 1901 by Hugo de Vries who had been researching the subject in his work about mutations — a subject discussed below. Yet Mendel's papers were published in a periodical which was circulated to libraries and universities around the world. It can only be inferred that they were deliberataly ignored as they flatly contradicted Darwin's theory which had been launched only seven years before in a furore of controversy. The evidence Mendel reported was not welcomed by evolutionists, and there were a number of them at that time in senior positions in the scientific establishment (such as the 'X' Club [26p112f]) who would be unwilling to give them any publicity.

It was only when de Vries claimed that genetic information could be modified from one generation to the next by mutation that Mendel's results could be 'rediscovered' and given some publicity.

The interesting thing is that the results that Mendel published to prove his theory were actually 'too good to be true'. His figures were examined [Annals of Science v1 p115], and it was found that statistically the deviation from the perfect ratios of the various groups was far smaller than he should really have obtained in practice. This is not to say that his theory was wrong, but he seems to have known what the ratios should be and accordingly 'fudged' his results to be close to the values he was expecting!

2. LIMITS TO BREEDING

When discussing the evidence against evolution, often the wide variety of dogs is presented as support for the theory — usually with the comment that if man can breed such a variety in a few years then nature could produce a new species given millions of years. The answer to this is that they are all still dogs, no new species have been produced and all are capable of breeding with each other to produce fertile offspring.

Breeders of any animals are fully aware that they cannot breed them beyond certain limits. Race horse owners inbreed fast horses to produce even faster runners. Beyond a certain limit however they find that the offspring develop problems with their leg joints and many other difficulties arise. They then have to breed them with good original stock. It is for this reason that rich American racehorse breeders are willing to pay high prices for good Irish and English horses.

Another result of inbreeding to produce specialised features is that the range of characters that can be developed is reduced. This is known as a reduction in the 'gene pool', i.e. some genes have been emphasised, and others have been reduced in their effectiveness or bred out of the specialised group. The result of this can be that when two very specialised breeds, say of a Great Dane and a St. Bernard are crossed, the offspring may suffer from serious deficiencies, as the result of excessive inbreeding.

Darwin, in the course of his work on evolution took up the breeding of pigeons to study the variation of species. It is well known amongst breeders of all animals that whilst there is a wide variety of types which have been developed from one basic stock or specie, nevertheless, there is a definite limit to what could be achieved. This was a most serious obstacle to his theory. How did he deal with it? He simply ignored it, for in his book 'The Origin of Species' he deals with the problem in one short paragraph towards the end of his first chapter. He states that it was ' ... rash to assert that a limit had been attained in any one case'

and that

'It would be equally rash to assert that characters ... could not, after remaining fixed for many centuries, again vary under new conditions of life' [27p48].

Thus he brushed aside all the evidence of the stability of species and based his theory on a pure speculation, which I have shown in diagramatic form in Fig. 11. Yet he nevertheless claimed that his theory was scientific, a claim his followers still make today.

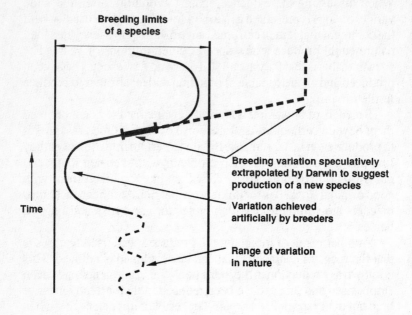

Fig. 11. Darwin's speculation on breeding a species.

Variations in nature.

As evolution depends upon variations taking place over a long time, all changes are claimed as evidence of evolution. Differing environmental influences can affect the specific characteristics of a population. For example, the average (say of size) may be altered in one direction, or the range may be made smaller, or the extremes may increase tending to give two separate varieties. This is then said to show how species change (and evolve) under environmental pressures. What they fail to show is that when the conditions return to normal, the range of characteristics also returns to what it was originally [28p188]. There are therefore strong pressures that maintain the stability of a species.

In addition to this stability, it has been found that in some flies at least there is a behaviour pattern that maintains the range of variations possessed by the species. There is a tendency to mate more frequently with those flies who have genetic material that occurs less frequently in the group. This ensures that the full range of genes is available to the species, which would allow it to survive differing conditions. If those flies with the more rare genetic material were mated with *less* frequently, then these characteristics could eventually be lost from the 'gene pool'. Whether this interesting feature applies to groups other than flies has yet to be determined [28p194].

'Macroevolution' and 'Microevolution'

The variation within a species is sometime referred to as 'microevolution', whilst the development of one species from another is called 'macro-evolution'. Some creationists accept that 'microevolution' has occured in nature, but not 'macro-evolution', and these terms are often used in creationist literature. The use of the phrase 'micro-evolution' by creationists is surely unwise because it implies that *some* degree of evolution has taken place, a concept that might be assumed by a reader who lacks some background knowledge. It suggests that it is only a question of degree between micro- and macro-evolution, and the line may be drawn in different positions depending upon your viewpoint. There are, however, clear limits to the breeding of any species, and for changes within a species, 'variation' is a far more accurate word to use. I would therefore urge creationists not to refer to either micro- or macro-evolution as being potentially misleading, but to use the terms 'evolution' (for the emergence of species) and 'variation' (for changes within a species).

3. MUTATIONS INADEQUATE

It is the occasional mutation which appears in all species that is claimed to be the way in which new features can be introduced into an evolving species. Yet numerous genetic experiments have been carried out — many of them on a small fruit fly called Drosophila melanogaster — but a viable new form has not been achieved.

Experimenters have subjected the unfortunate creature to heat, X-rays, Gamma-rays, mustard gas and many other agents that affect the genetic coding as it has been found that these greatly increase the number of mutations. Quite distorted forms have been produced; some have twisted bodies, some are blind, others without wings, etc. whilst the most grotesque have a leg growing from the lip or even out of the eye.

The normal fly has about 36 bristles on its body and some experiments were conducted to try see how many or how few could be reached by breeding. After several generations an upper limit of 56 and a lower limit of 25 was achieved, but beyond this the flies began to die rapidly. When they were allowed to breed freely, the bristle count eventually returned to the normal number.

In another experiment, eyeless flies were mated and the offsping were also eyeless. This continued for several generations, when unexpectedly flies with eyes began to appear. This suggested that there was some means by which the genes were able to repair deficiencies, or that even severely repressed characteristics can eventually re-emerge. Eyelessness can also be due to a mutation in one controlling gene, which may mutate back to its original form.

All this effort has undoubtedly led to a great increase in our knowledge of genetics, but it still does not support the theory of evolution for no new true species has been produced. Indeed it has been admitted that none of the mutations could survive under natural conditions.

It is obvious that the production of mutations are the result of damage to the genetic code; damage which results in a distorted body quite unfit to survive. Indeed, the reliance of evolutionists upon damaging mutations as the means by which evolution progresses is rather like saying that using a hammer on a number of delicate watches will eventually improve one of them!

The inability of mutations to provide a mechanism for the progress of evolution is admitted in no less a publication than one produced by the British Natural History Museum and written by a member of their staff. In 'Evolution' [11] written by Colin Patterson, the admission is made that

'... a favourable mutation conferring a 1% advantage ... may have to occur about fifty times before, by chance, it becomes sufficiently widespread in the population to have a secure future'.

In this publication there is an even more damaging admission which effectively destroys the whole basis of the reliance of evolution on mutations for he says;

'The problem is that natural selection theory says that very small selection coefficients, of the order of 1% or less, are effective in causing evolutionary changes, yet the demonstration of such small differences in fitness is simply not possible in experiments. It has been calculated that a 1% difference in fertility between two genotypes could be shown with 95% confidence only if the fertility of 130,000 females of each type were measured. If only the fertility of 380 females of each type were measured, the investigator has only an even chance of detecting a much larger difference in fertility of 10%. *So selection theory is trapped in its own sophistication: its asserts that small differences in fitness are effective agents of evolutionary change, yet differences of that order are not detectable in practice.*' [11p69]

When one considers that mutations are rare, almost every one of them is injurious, and that the the same beneficial mutation has to occur a number of times to get it established in the species, then it can be seen just how unlikely it is that a new species could evolve quickly enough by this method in rapidly changing environmental conditions. The mutation theory just does not work and is but one more inadequate attempt to provide a mechanism of how new species can arise.

The final blow to the theory is that de Vries' original experiments on mutation in plants have been repeated, only to find that the new characteristics he reported were actually in the parents already [29p588].

4. MATHEMATICAL THEORIES

If we examine the simple table of possible arrangements of inherited Mendelian characteristics as shown in Fig 10, it is obvious that they are a simple matter of mathematical probability. If we take this aspect further, we can provide mathematical theories for a characteristic that has entered into a species by mutation and predict how it may possibly increase in frequency (if it occurs sufficiently often) or be swamped by the natural gene pool of the greater majority of the population. Patterson gives a lengthy description of this subject complete with graphs of how a mutation can spread throughout a population [11p56-75]

Much of this however is based upon one characteristic being represented by one gene, which, as we have already pointed out, is a very simplified picture of the true situation. Patterson himself at the end of his chapter reminds his readers that genes are part of the whole chromosome, and a characteristic may be influenced by many other parts of the chromosome, by translocations, by adjacent genes etc. and therefore even how a characteristic arises is complex and not as yet fully understood. Thus, all mathematical theories, no matter how complex, are based on assumptions which are a gross oversimplification, and will therefore give answers whose accuracy are hardly worth the effort and time spent upon them.

Despite this, the subject has blossomed into a very esoteric discipline, filled with much mathematical formulae that are understood by few outside the inner court of the high priests of this subject. One who has examined the subject for its practical outworkings is Norman Macbeth who became severely critical of its experts in his book 'Darwin Retried' [30].

In a chapter entitled 'Natural Selection', he reproduces two examples of the writings of mathematical geneticists (Fisher and Sewall Wright) that I am sure to the vast majority of readers is completely unintelligible. Macbeth surmises that they are 'comprehensible to not more than one reader in a hundred and one biologist in ten.' [30p51] — a very generous proportion in my estimation.

He concludes the chapter with a scathing criticism, saying —

'I would even like to suggest that the American Institute of Biological Sciences appoint a commission of competent biologists to review all the work of Fisher, Ford, Haldane and Wright and decide whether it has added anything whatever to our understanding of nature. This is not as mad as it sounds, because we have been through all this before. Sir Julian Huxley, doubtless aided by his long family memory, reports that Francis Galton (Darwin's cousin) and his disciple Karl Pearson, in the early days, applied mathematical methods of extreme delicacy and ingenuity to the study of evolutionary problems. In vain. They were working from assumptions that proved to be erroneous, and all their labours were useless. Huxley thinks it is different now because the present mathematicians are working on "a firm basis of fact," but the day may come when their facts are seen to be erroneous assumptions and their labours go into the wastebasket.' [30p52]

We will be referring to these theories again when dealing with the subject of Peppered Moths and industrial melanism in Appendix 2.

[I would mention in passing that Macbeth, with his training as a lawyer, has written an excellent book that is very critical of the whole basis of the theory of evolution. Despite this, he nevertheless maintained that evolution had actually taken place, and it was simply that it needed a better theoretical basis and more convincing evidence.

Did he just give lip service to the theory in order to be more acceptable to the academic world? I could not help noticing that in describing the sophisticated feeding habits of a caterpillar, he comments ' ... 'the whole performance shows a master hand.' [30p71]. Was he here revealing the true position from which he was making his criticisms? I cannot help suspecting that he may have been a 'sheep in wolf's clothing' or a 'mole' in the evolutionary establishment.]

Macbeth is not the only legal expert to criticise the lines of reasoning used by evolutionists. More recently, Professor Philip Johnson, who teaches Law at the University of California at Berkeley, has, in his book 'Darwin on Trial' (Regnery Gateway 1991), rigorously exposed the inadequacy of the arguments used by evolutionists on a wide range of subjects.

5. POLYPLOIDY IN PLANTS

It has been found that with some plants, similar species can interbreed but the resulting mixed plant (a hybrid) is sterile, i.e. it will not reproduce itself when fertilised. This is because the chromosome pairs do not match when the germ cells are being formed. Occasionaly however, the hybrid divides the chromosomes but not the nucleus, thus producing germ cells with twice the number of chromosomes to that of the parents. These new plants they give rise to can interbreed with each other but are sterile with both the parents and are therefore classed as a new species.

This unusual form of division occasionaly takes place in nature but can be induced by chemicals such as colchicine in the laboratory. It is due to this chromosome doubling that many flowering plants and cereals etc. have been produced. They are usually larger, more colourful etc. than the parents and could be likened to having a 'double dose' of the genetic ingredients which produce these heightened features.

The main objection is that polyploidy produces no *new* characteristics whatsoever. All that has happened is the 'heightening' of certain features already in the parents. In addition, whilst polyploidy has been of great value to humans in the production of better plants and cereals, cases of polyploidy in animals is confined mainly to a few worms, insects etc. that are self fertilising. It has played no significant part in the evolution of the animal kingdom.

6. BACTERIA AND VIRUSES

Bacteria are extremely small single cells, the majority of which rely upon other organisms to provide the source of their food. They are often found associated with the decomposition of organic matter, and in that way are important in recycling material in the complex network of the food chain. Some bacteria are harmful however as we well know when human tissue is infected. Classifying bacteria is difficult and this is usually done by their individual shapes and other features, so that the use of the term 'species', 'genera' etc. for these organisms is not the same as in the animal world.

Bacteria are able to divide rapidly to form new cells, and from one cell a colony can grow at an incredible rate, in the order of 16 million in one day. One expert has calculated that, provided conditions are ideal for reproduction, within 36 hours one cell could multiply enough times to cover the whole earth with a layer one foot deep [31].

Bacteria also have a wide range of variability. So much so that it is sometimes difficult to distinguish where one 'species' begins and another ends. This variation is the main problem that doctors have in trying to find a solution to many bacterial infections for each one usually requires a specific antibiotic to combat it.

With such a high rate of reproduction with variation, this should be an ideal situation to watch evolution in action and see if a completely different form of bacteria can arise. With all the investigations that have been carried out, however, on these organisms over more than one hundred years, a pure colony of bacteria has not been able to vary beyond certain limits. Thus these minute cells exhibit the same inherent natural limits to their development as we have seen applies in the animal world. [32].

When bacteria are attacked by antibiotics they often develop a new strain that is resistant to them and can then multiply to form a new colony. This is claimed to be an example of a hostile environment bringing about new mutations that allow the organism to 'evolve' to a new form.

What actually happens is as follows. Antibiotic resistant individuals in bacterial populations carry plasmids. These are circular DNA molecules that code for certain enzymes that are part of the function of the bacteria. These enzymes, however, are also able to catalyse the breakdown of the antibiotics which is a function they are able to perform that is purely coincidental. What is interesting is that bacterial cultures from bodies frozen 140 years ago were found to be resistant to antibiotics that were developed 100 years later. Thus the specific chemical needed for resistance was inherent in the bacteria.

In addition, the surviving strains are usually less virulent, and have a reduced metabolism and so grow more slowly. This is hardly a recommendation for 'improving the species by competition' (i.e. suvival of the fittest).

Finally, they are still the same bacteria and of the same type, being only a variety that differs from the normal in its resistance to the antibiotic. No new 'species' have been produced.

Viruses

These are even smaller than bacteria, being a bundle of complex biochemicals such as RNA and DNA. It is sometimes inferred (by perhaps putting them as the first picture in the evolutionary chain) that as they are only one stage removed from a large chemical molecule that could be synthesised in a laboratory, then they are likely to be the precursors of the 'simple cell'. This could not possibly be, however, for no virus is able to reproduce itself outside of a living cell. In actual fact, it is not the virus which copies itself, it is the cell which manufactures copies of it. It could not therefore have existed before there were any cells which were necessary for its reproduction.

B. PRESENT DAY EVOLUTION

It is obvious that if evolution has been proceeding for millions of years, then one would expect to see numerous cases where is it still operating and changing the characteristics of animals around us. However, such evidence is not immediately apparent. When challenged about this the usual reply of evolutionists is that the process is too slow to produce a noticeable difference over just a few hundred years, say. Yet again, the vital evidence just happens to be unavailable!

Evolutionists were keen to demonstrate that evolution was actually taking place even today, and one species was known to have changed within recorded memory, and this we examine below. We will also consider another example where the evidence supposed to support evolution has come to light in comparatively recent times.

1. PEPPERED MOTH

The Peppered moth, species Biston betularia, has three forms, a light speckled variety (typica), which is the most common, a much darker speckled form (insularia) and very dark (carbonaria). When the Industrial Revolution took place, the soot generated by the factories darkened the bark of the trees around heavy industrial areas such as Manchester. At the same time, a rise in the number of the dark form was noted and it was contended that the reason was that the light variety was more conspicuous than the dark and was therefore captured by birds. The dark variety consequently grew in numbers and became the main form in some areas.

The evidence was claimed to be confirmed by tests carried out by Dr. H.B.D. Kettlewell in which moths were released in a polluted and unpolluted wood and the numbers of the varieties recaptured were noted.

It is therefore confidently asserted that it was the industrial blackening of the trees that gave the dark variety an advantage over the light variety. This evidence of a variety conferring an advantage under certain conditions is claimed to illustrate evolution in action.

But is this conclusion, which is so widely publicised in all books on evolution, as simple as that? As with all evidence that seems to support evolution so strongly, a closer examination does not just damage the case presented, but finally destroys it.

The first major criticism is that the dark form is still only a variety of the same moth. The appearance of the dark moth is probably due to normal variation, and not necessarily a mutation. Similar dark varieties have been found in other types of moths. In fact, there is no way of determining whether a feature is due to a mutation or an original, but rare, component of the genetic potential. Albinism — a loss of colouration — is a reverse case of a similar form of variety.

A second criticism is that the dark form is found living quite happily in a rural environment in Scotland, Canada and New Zealand, where it presumably enjoys no particular advantage. Patterson, in his book 'Evolution' [11], also mentions that more than a hundred insect species in Britain alone show similar changes due to a variety of genetic factors. Both varieties are sustained, he says, ' ... providing a ready source of variation if pollution increases'. Yet if we apply the theory of 'survival of the fittest' to these dark forms in a light environment, they should have been eliminated quite quickly. No evolutionist's explanation for this aspect has ever been given.

The final and most serious criticism is of the serious deficiencies of Kettlewell's experiments in which marked moths were released in polluted and unpolluted woods. The reports of these experiments have been carefully examined by Prof. Sermonti who forwarded me a copy of his article that later appeared in the Italian biology periodical 'Rivista di Biologia' [33]. His criticisms are very damaging, and I have examined the whole subject of these experiments in Appendix 3.

Summarising all the relevant evidence, by far the most likely cause of the increase of the dark variety, is not that they possessed an evolutionary advantage, but that they migrated into these areas over a period of years. There is indeed some evidence for this. Dr. Colin Patterson notes that the change was observed not only in the industrial areas but ' ... also in some nearby rural, unpolluted areas' [11p81].

Thus the much vaunted 'Peppered Moths' evidence for 'evolution in action' is seen to be based more upon wishful thinking than anything else. The supporting evidence was obtained from a series of experiments which, in Appendix 3, I will try to show were virtually contrived to give the answers being sought, but which actually gave results that were either inconclusive or even contradictory.

2. SICKLE-CELL ANAEMIA

There is a mutation in some people which results in some of their blood cells becoming shaped like a sickle instead of the normal flat disc shape. It is due to one of the pair of chromosomes having the defective gene. It has been found that those who have this feature are not affected by a particular form of malaria which can at times be fatal. This results in a larger proportion of people with this mutation being able to live in an area where this disease is prevalent in Africa.

Sickle cell anaemia is therefore hailed as an example of a mutation conferring a benefit upon the holder. As we have discussed above, a sufficient accumulation of these over a long period of time is considered to provide an adequate explanation of how life has adapted to changes in the environment.

The most serious objection to this evidence is those who are unfortunate enough to have sickle cell anaemia suffer very distressing spasmodic breathing attacks and often die before adolescence [34]. Thus, far from being a 'benefit', sickle-cell anaemia is actually a severe disadvantage. The immunity it provides to a particular form of malaria is only a by-product of the lower efficiency of the blood cells that the carrier has, and it is this weakness that can be fatal.

This example of the supposed benefits that sickle cell anaemia confers is so frequently quoted in support of evolution and as an example of a good mutation that it will be as well to demonstrate its inadequacies by an illustration. Imagine a line of identical cars (= a complicated organism). Each one of them is to be hit only once by a large sledge hammer (= random genetic change producing mutations). Some cars are little affected, some more so, whilst others fail to go at all after such treatment. One car however sustains damage in the carburettor in such a way that it goes along only very quietly (and slowly). The manufacturers may try to publicise the new model as a 'super quiet' model, but the public are unlikely to be impressed when they find that it only goes at 5 m.p.h!

In a similar way regarding sickle cell anaemia, the much publicised 'advantage' of the malaria protection is far outweighed by the resulting physical disabilities that it also brings.

C. RECAPITULATION.

This is a theory that was much in vogue at the end of the last century. The idea was that the development of the foetus of animals went through the evolutionary stages of its ancestors. Thus the beginning of life was a single cell and this is reflected in the foetus starting as one cell also. The development of fish in the sea is paralleled by the water surrounding the foetus in the mother and similarly, the creases in the neck of the human foetus (Fig. 12) where the gills are in fish was considered to be evidence of man's 'fishy' ancestry — if you will forgive the pun!

1) HAECKEL'S FORGERIES

The theory was greatly publicised in Germany by Prof. Haeckel who produced drawings of the various stages of the development of the embryos of different animals, and showed how very much alike they were. The implication was of course that they had a common ancestry. In an excellent article [35], Rusch has exposed the fact that Haeckel's evidence was fraudulent. He made three identical woodcuts of an ovum and labelled them as being those of a dog, a monkey and a man. He similarly used the same woodcut of a blastula (a later stage in the development of the embryo) and labelled them as being from a dog, a chicken and a tortoise. These drawings, and others that he had 'ajusted' were noted by his academic colleagues and he was called before a university court in Jena where he admitted that he had 'doctored' his evidence.

2) ERRONEOUS THEORY ADMITTED

The theory received considerable publicity, and many experts constructed a detailed sequence of the evolution of an animal simply by studying the stages in the development of its foetus. This sequence however often contradicted the one derived from a study of the fossil evidence. Gradually the patient efforts of other workers proved that the whole theory was quite baseless, and this was acknowledged by evolutionists themselves. Sir Gavin de Beer of the British Natural History Museum admitted —

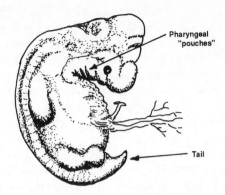

Fig. 12. The human embryo and the neck creases.

'Seldom has an assertion like that of Haeckel's "theory of recapitulation", facile, tidy and plausible, widely accepted without critical examination, done so much harm to science' [36p159]

This particular theory provided such a good weapon of propaganda for the evolutionists that, although they very reluctantly abandoned it in the face of irrefutable facts, they nevertheless still refer to it in oblique ways, and at times not even that. For example, 'gill pouches' and 'vestigial tails' may still be mentioned when dealing with human embryos, or the early embryonic stages of different species may be pictured, usually one of them being that of a human, and the reader is invited to 'note the similarities'. All this is done to imply our links with other animals, despite the fact that experts can tell at an early stage the difference between various classes.

A classic example of this appears in one book on evolution [37] that gives simplified pictures of the embryos of five animals and man, and the text below reads as follows.

'Embryology reveals remarkable similarity of structure between animals ... Darwin was the first to point out the reason. If embryos are similar they must have descended from a common ancestor, from which they have inherited the embryonic stages repeated in their own development. It was suggested that during its embryonic development every individual goes through the stages by which it evolved from a primitive form. This is considered today rather an exaggeration but in the embryos of most vertebrates, at comparable stages, they all have fish-like characteristics, with gill pouches or slits in the head...The gill pouches are more aptly called visceral clefts as they never truly function as gills, but are served in the early stages by arteries undoubtedly homologous with those of an adult fish ... ' [37p26]

A careful reading of this passage is interesting. That the theory of recapitulation is incorrect is acknowledged, but instead of admitting that it was actually erroneous, it is briefly described as 'an exaggeration'. Despite this, the whole tenor of the section following is worded to suggest strongly that embryos *do* go through stages of their ancestor's evolution with such phrases as 'fish-like characteristics', 'gill slits', 'homologous with those of an adult fish' etc. Although the writer does not even have the cake, she nevertheless still wants the reader to eat it!

The phrase 'It was at one time thought ... ' gives a picture of some scientists indulging in some speculations from their armchairs on the similarities that they could see in these embryos. In fact, it was a strongly held theory that was given a great deal of publicity, wasted hundreds of hours of expensive laboratory time and about which many books and papers were written. It took the patient work of serious scientists to disprove the reckless statements of Haeckel and others on this subject.

It may be wondered why a theory that has been abandoned even by evolutionists is nevertheless being discussed in this book. One reason is to show how theories, accepted as 'incontrovertible fact' by one generation may be recognised as fallacies by the next. Another reason is that the theory, or a very similar one, is still sometimes taught by schoolteachers who have failed to realise that it is out of date. This is due to the lack of publicity which is given to evidence that contradicts evolution (or in this case false evidence that was at one time used to support it). As a result, schools continue to teach outmoded ideas and it can take many years before the textbooks catch up with the latest view.

I mention this aspect because during a lecture at a school about the evidence against evolution I referred to the fact that the recapitulation theory was now discredited even by evolutionists. A teacher who was present expressed her suprise as she had regularly taught the subject in her biology classes. When she later checked it, she admitted that what she had been teaching her pupils for many years was incorrect. It is to be hoped that others reading this book will be similarly prepared to check their facts on other topics pertaining to evolution, and amend their teaching accordingly.

3. PAEDOMORPHISM

Another theory similar to that of recapitulation is Paedomorphism. This asserts that species who evolve are sometimes similar to the young of its ancestors. In the evolution of man, the most frequently quoted example is to note that the rounded shape of the human skull is similar to the skulls of young chimpanzees, Neanderthal fossil skulls and Australopithecine fossil apes (a so-called missing link). In this case the human development is said to have been 'arrested' when the species was evolving, and as the human line 'never grew up', it is sometimes known as 'Peter Pan' evolution.

There is no biological evidence whatsoever that this has ever taken place, or even that it could actually take place at all. The whole theory is simply based on the observation of the similarity of the rounded skulls of the young of some species and the adult form of others.

There must obviously be numerous coincidental similarities between the many millions of species, and Paedomorphism has selected just one specific feature — the roundness of the skulls. Despite the lack of any evidence, the confident assertion of Paedomorphism as if it were a fact is yet another example of the way in which even the weakest case is used to persuade an unsuspecting public that there is 'scientific proof' of evolution.

Gavin de Beer, in a 1964 publication of the Natural History Museum entitled 'Evolution' [87] claimed that the caterpillars of moths and the larvae of starfish were examples of the young forms undergoing their own evolution without affecting the structure of the adults [p26]. To believe that the young could change without having any effect upon their own adult form is surely to engage in an unjustifiable leap of faith. He further says that as the young have soft bodies, animals that developed by paedomorphism would have a gap in the fossil record! The whole theory is very superficial, and we will be considering the phenomenal changes that are involved in the tranformation of a caterpillar to a moth in section II E 2.

Whilst referring to this early (1964) exposition of evolutionary propaganda by de Beer, it is interesting to compare some of the bold claims it makes with those of more recent publications. In this book, the typical geological column of the fossils with a time scale is given, and the text of the book gives evidence for the gradual transformation of one species into another.

By contrast, the more recent (1981) publication 'Origin of Species' by the Natural History Museum specifically states 'Throughout the book, the emphasis is on living species, and no attempt is made to reconstruct the history of life on Earth. Moreover, the treatment of genetics is confined to what is needed for a basic understanding of variations and inheritance.' [12p5]. The book's main emphasis is on the 'relationships' between species, which are displayed by the many cladogram diagrams it presents. No reference is made to the gradual 'links' between species which were given in the older book. In their summary, it is even admitted that in some cases 'the theory is difficult to apply' and in other cases 'the theory doesn't seem to explain the situation — at least not very well'.

This is certainly a far more cautious approach to the whole subject of evolution than has usually been displayed.

D. CLASSIFICATION

In the first chapter of Genesis, it says that animals will only breed 'after their kind'. This means that no section of a 'kind' will ever develop into another 'kind', i.e. there will be no evolution across these boundaries. It is tempting to presume that these 'kinds' are the same group as we nowadays call a species, but as we have seen, geneticists cannot define a species accurately, and this suggests that the 'kinds' may be larger groups than our classification of species.

The first person to attempt a scientific classification of animals was Carl Linnaeus of Sweden. He tried to discover which animal and plant groups could be put together to form these 'kinds'. The task was extremely difficult and still is today, for there are several ways in which classifications can be made. Linnaeus' lists however became the basis of modern classification and furthermore it was found that they could be arranged in a 'progressive' series which was considered as evidence for evolution.

1. HOMOLOGY (SIMILARITY OF SOME SPECIES)

One of the major arguments used to support the theory of evolution is to point out that many groups of species have the same basic pattern to their body, particularly the form of their skeletons. Most mammals, birds, bats, and whales etc. have the same basic arrangement of a skull on the end of the spine, a rib cage and four limbs, each of the limbs usually having five sets of bones (the pentadactyl limb) at their ends. Such a close similarity is then said to be clear evidence that they have all evolved from either a common ancestor or the basic pattern was passed on from generation to generation. In books this claim is usually accompanied by a diagram showing the similarity of the pentadactyl limbs of a bat's wing, a whale's flipper, and a human arm and hand.

This would appear to a reasonable argument, but as always, there is an alternative explanation, and which one you accept and which you reject depends entirely upon the philosophical position from which you approach the subject of evolution.

It must first be pointed out that all arrangements of a series or similarities are the specific choice of a person who has selected his examples from a wide range of possible varieties that he could have chosen. It is he who has decided the particular characteristic he wishes to emphasise (or theory he wants to prove).

In the case of the similarities (homologies) between different species, the evolutionist wants to prove that they are the result of all having a common ancestor. No one was there at the time this ancestor existed, and therefore the evidence produced is purely circumstantial. Therefore, in order to prove that certain species had a common origin, those with similar features are selected and, based upon this evidence, are claimed to be related.

But there are many instances that could be quoted of animals that look similar or share very similar features that on closer investigation are certainly not related in many other fundamental aspects. One example is we have already examined the horse 'series', and another is bird classification which will be examined later. A further example that has been quoted is the similarity between the claws of a cat, our fingernails, and the hoofs of a horse. Here again, although these similarities exist, the evolutionist is unable to point to any series of living or fossilised animals that could possibly form any link between them.

Therefore all that can be said when we look at these homologies is that some species have similar features, *and that is all.* There is no warrant to extend this argument to claim that they are therefore descended from a common ancestor, for as we have shown, the principle cannot be applied universally. Therefore to use it in the case of the similarities of the skeletal frame of all mammals may appear convincing, but is equally unacceptable as it is far from being a universal law.

If we consider the usual case that is presented that we have mentioned (that of the similarities of the bat, whale and human frame) the point we are trying to make can be demonstrated using this very example. It is quoted in books in order to 'prove' that they are connected by a common ancestor. It is stretching the fossil record too far to provide a series between this hypothetical ancestor and both bats and humans. To attempt to do so between whales and *any* other mammal is quite impossible as we will see later. There-fore, the similarity of the skeletons is no proof of any evolutionary relationship whatsoever. Indeed the frame is about the only feature that is common between them — numerous chemical and functional features in these three mammals are completely different. These differences are so great that quite different classifications could be drawn up using various criteria, but this is a subject dealt with later in the section entitled 'Molecular evidence'.

The fact that many animals share a number of similar features could be explained just as well by accepting that the Creator used a satisfactory basic pattern, and that He varied this form over a very wide range of proportions in His design of many of the animals that He produced. If a standard skeletal frame could function equally well for a bat as for a whale, each one being carefully proportioned to suit the animal's environment and size, then why should the Creator be expected to have a completely different layout for every different species ?

Creatures are full of evidence of God's 'economy of design', i.e. one organ or chemical, with only slight modifications, can be used for a completely different function. God has used similar patterns where they could be used, yet as we can see, He has also created a staggering variety of other forms of life on this planet. There are many organic and biochemical similarities between species that appear completely different, but there are also these similar patterns in a wide range of species.

Many biologists, biochemists and doctors — indeed anyone who has studied the intricacies of animals or humans in detail — have been struck by the complex yet exquisite design apparent in the workings of living organisms. Faced with this evidence in their own field, it is surprising that some will still nevertheless contend that it is a result of chance incidents that took place over millions of years.

Embryological evidence.

Thus far, the arguments are of a more philosophical nature, and each individual will draw his own conclusions, which, as we have suggested, will depend more upon his preconceptions than upon reason. The arguments presented, however, cannot be labelled scientific, and creationists have had some difficulty in countering this seemingly plausible support for the evolution of many animals from some common origin. There is however evidence from one discipline that completely refutes the concept that the similarity of organs and limbs is effective proof of a common ancestor.

If we take as an example the supposed tranformation of a reptile's scale into a bird's feather, then this must be the same organ that is gradually changed by small mutations over many genera-tions. But, as was mentioned when dealing with Archaeopteryx, a study of the embryos of reptiles and birds has shown that scales arise from a section of the embryo of a reptile that is completely different from the section of a bird's embryo from which its feathers arise from. Thus, far from one feature being modified, these very special organs have a quite distinct origin in the embryo, and cannot therefore have gradually changed from one shape or function to another.

Although not an example of homology, I have used this example of scales and feathers as it can be easily understood, but this can be taken much further, for very surprisingly, there are many seemingly identical organs that originate from totally different parts of the embryos.

A study by De Beer of the development of the embryos of quite similar animals and insects showed that in many cases virtually identical organs in each of the differing species actually develop from completely different parts of the embryo [38]. For example, in man, the arm develops from segments 13 to 18 in the embryo, whilst in the newt, they come from segments 9 to 11. In the lizard it arises from segments 6 to 9, and many such instances of the different origin of similar organs could be given. De Beer also qoutes examples of species of animals or insects that appear to be almost identical in the adult form, yet which have a considerably different embryonic development.

De Beer noted that ' ... correspondence between homologous structures cannot be pressed back to similarity of position of the cells of the embryo or the parts of the egg out of which these structures are differentiated.' [38]

This evidence therefore demolishes both the supposed gradual 'adaptation' of certain organs for another purpose, and the assumption that similarity of shape (homology) between species is evidence that they shared a common ancestor.

2. CONVERGENT EVOLUTION.

There are many species that are not closely related, but that nevertheless have one or more very specific features in common. Examples of this would be the blood sucking of leeches, ticks, larvae and other organisms, or the ability of several plants to trap and digest small insects, etc. The Nautilus is a floating sea shell but it has eyes very similar to vertebrates with a 'pinhole camera' for forming the image, a retina, a spherical shape for swivelling in the socket etc. How did it come to evolve this amazing organ at such an early stage of the progress of evolution? Many other examples could be given of such 'convergent evolution'.

In all these cases, the evolutionist has to believe that although such highly specialised structures have evolved completely independantly from each other, they have resulted in almost identical forms. In each case the particular feature is fully developed and not rudimentary. It is far easier to accept the fact that the animal's organs have been designed complete with their specific abilities rather than have to maintain that they have evolved several times in different animals to result in the same basic organ.

This use of the words 'convergent evolution' to describe this unusual repition of specialised characteristics, is a classic example of the way in which the evolutionist is forced to explain *every* feature of the natural world as complying with his theory. Unusual repetition of specialised characteristics, is a classic example. To evolve one special organ such as the eye is a major problem. To find that this has evolved quite independently more than once requires even more credulity in those who believe in evolution. To make such faith easier, it is given the title of 'convergent evolution' as if applying this label is sufficient to dismiss the problem that it really conceals.

It is obvious that life appears in a phenomenally diverse range, and it is this fact that enables evolutionists to select a particular feature and arrange it into a series in order to support their theory. Many of the links or inferences that are claimed do not actually exist in practice and are quite spurious.

It is little wonder that the subject is not dwelt upon at any length in text books on evolution. Indeed, it might almost be taken as a fair indication that where a subject is only mentioned and glossed over quickly, that the basic concept is actually a major stumbling block to the theory. However, a few moments consideration by any thoughtful reader on what is really implied would bring this fact out into the open, where it should rightly be.

3. DARWIN'S GALAPAGOS FINCHES

Darwin consistently claimed that it was while he was on the Galapagos islands that he first thought about evolution. He showed that the finches on the different islands had developed in various ways and he suggested that they had become separate species.

Despite this confident assertion, it is recorded that while he was actually on the island he completely failed to notice the similarities of the finches. This similarity, as well as the difference in their beaks, was *not* recognised by Darwin at all. These features were pointed out to him several months after his arrival in England by an ornithologist who had been entrusted with examining the birds [39p229].

With regard to the evidence itself, the birds that inhabit the islands have been given the names of separate species based upon very small differences of beak size and shape, plumage etc. From this, it is held that distinct species can arise from a root stock.

Lammerts however has carefully measured and described these characteristics [40p354f], and concluded that the range of features displayed in Darwin's finches are a continuum that is virtually unbroken. He also refers to the wide diversification of the American song sparrow, which showed a remarkably similar range of features arising from one species.

The only obviously different species on these islands is the Warbler finch which has distinct feeding habits also. These are almost certainly a quite separate migration of some birds from the mainland and have no genetic connection with Darwin's finches. Lammerts makes the interesting claim that the differing feeding habits are a *result* of the various shapes of bills that the individuals inherited, and are *not* 'adaptive divergencies' resulting from natural selection.

As there are no clear boundaries between the limits of the range of Darwin's finches, this suggests that what are labelled as separate species are simply a diversification from one basic species that has developed various shapes of beaks and plumage — just as a wide diversity can be obtained in the breeding of dogs. In this case, no separate species has been developed. Therefore, their much vaunted claim to be the very first evidence of evolution that prompted Darwin to propose his theory is invalid.

4. BIRD CLASSIFICATIONS

There are several areas of biology that books on evolution only deal with briefly because they provide little or no evidence for the theory or even contradict it. As so often occurs, it is not the evidence that a book provides which is important, it is the facts that are quietly ignored that are even more revealing. This would apply to the classification of existing birds.

One ornithologist has admitted that the classification of birds is one of the most difficult tasks to undertake. Examination of charts giving a 'tree' of their evolution will be found to have the existing birds only appearing at the end of the 'branches', with none of the intermediate forms appearing at the points where the branches divide. This is claimed to be due to the 'few fossil remains' but it could be asked why there should be so few fossils of birds, for their chances of being fossilised are just as likely (or unlikely) as animals.

The real problem facing those who try to classify birds is not the lack of fossil evidence but the total confusion of several important characteristics in living species.

Birds have a number of distinct features. For example there are five types of skulls, some have hollow bones, others do not, some have a special oil gland above the tail, others have powder down feathers which provide a sheen to the plumage, and there are different types of vocal chords etc. Now if a bird were to evolve the very special powder down feather, then you would expect all future species stemming from it to possess this feature. However this feature is found in a number of widely different types. To suggest that it evolved independently not once or twice but many times over is difficult to accept.

This aspect of wide distibution applies to all the other special characteristics. Indeed they all appear throughout the bird world in a seemingly random fashion. Similar looking birds may have a quite different structure and set of special features. On the other hand, different looking birds may have one or more very specialised features in common. It is as though these special characteristics were like a pack of cards which have been dealt out in a random fashion ignoring any apparent similarity of the birds. It is this aspect that makes classification so difficult when it is based upon evolutionary presuppositions.

All this simply goes to show that far from evolving over a long period of time with beneficial characterisitics being retained by a group, birds have been created with a variety of possible features. These features are all designed to be adequate or beneficial for their environment, and indeed it is their wide range of plumage and songs that have given endless delight to mankind for generations.

5. CIRCUMPOLAR GULLS.

The Herring Gull breeds in Great Britain and very similar varieties exist in the northern hemisphere around the North Pole. If you follow such a circle going from east to west, the colour of the wings gradually becomes darker until, when you arrive back in this country, the wings are quite black and the bird is known as the Lesser Black-backed Gull. Here, the two types do not breed together and have different feeding habits etc. This is claimed to be evidence of a species developing over a period of time and forming two distinct species (Fig. 13).

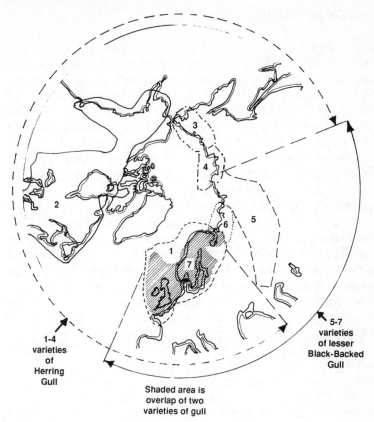

1-4
varieties
of
Herring
Gull

5-7
varieties
of lesser
Black-Backed
Gull

Shaded area is
overlap of two
varieties of gull

Fig. 13. Circumpolar Gulls.

However, it is admitted that the change in the name of the species at one point in the circle is 'arbitrary' [11p7]. The reason that they do not actually breed together is probably due to slight differences of habitat and breeding season as well as the distinctive colouring that would be looked for in a suitable mate. It is likely that they could breed together, by artificial insemination if needed, and still produce fertile offspring. The extremes of the range however may have lost sufficient genetic features from the basic 'gene pool' that offspring may not be healthy or even possible. This was previously considered in section A2 — Limits to breeding.

It is therefore justifiable to contend that all these birds are one species that exhibits a range of darkening of the wings and other characteristics. All these have simply been emphasised by in-breeding — just as special features have been obtained artificially in many domestic animals.

6. CICHLID FISHES

These are small fish that are found in Lake Victoria in East Africa. There are small differences between them and some 200 'species' have been identified. It is claimed that they are the result of separate species that inhabited small lakes in the area but over many years, these lakes enlarged and combined, providing the fish with a wider range of habitats that they could exploit. They therefore diversified and became so different that they could not interbreed. On this basis it is claimed that 'Now there are more than 200 species of cichlid fishes in Lake Victoria — each one slightly different from the others' [12p115]. There are in fact over 1000 'species' of these fresh water fish to be found in various lakes in the tropics.

In many cases, these slight differences are not sufficient to class them as separate species. To return to the well known situation of the population of dogs. Who would class a Great Dane as the same species as a minature Poodle? Yet there is no dispute that they are the same species. In the case of the cichlids, there may have been a few separate species that were similar looking, but the 200 referred to are simply varieties of the original stock. No new species has developed, for they are all still the same type of fish.

Dr. Arthur Jones carried out research on these fish [41] and after some three years concluded that despite a very wide range of characteristics and behaviour they were clearly all of the same family. He plotted the features of a large number of species and showed that they all shared numerous features in a mosaic-like pattern. The very wide range of colouring and patterns was the result of only a few basic colours and patterns, every variety being only a combination of these forms. These variations were distributed in a completely random fashion througout the whole family of fishes around the world, but they were all nevertheless the same family, with varieties labelled as 'species'.

It is interesting that there was a similar specific variety of behaviour patterns found within the family. For example, some varieties breed their infants in their mouth, but if infants from cichlids that breed normally are introduced to a mouth breeder, they quickly adapt to this strange form of breeding. The reverse also takes place with infants from mouth breeders being raised satisfactorily by a type of cichlid that does not take its young into its mouth. If on the other hand, similar looking young fish *from another family* are introduced to a mouth-breeding cichlid, there is total confusion and the process fails.

This clearly indicates that cichlid fish, even though they are not familiar with a particular behaviour pattern, nevertheless *do* recognise the other fish as being one of their own family, and therefore easily adapt themselves. There is no such adaptation to other fish even though they may have similar breeding patterns which they should have instinctively recognised. Following his extensive research on these fish, Dr. Jones eventually came to the conclusion that the family of cichlids may well be one of the 'kinds' referred to in Genesis Chapter 1.

[There is a very interesting sequel to this particular habit of mouth breeding by some cichlids. One type (Tilapia galileae), picks up a stone to fill its mouth when it eventually wants its growing offspring to leave. Denied access, the youngsters quickly learn to fend for themselves.

The reader is probably familiar with the account of Christ sending Peter to catch a fish that would have a coin for the Temple Tax in its mouth [Mat 17v24-27]. This particular fish is found in Lake Galilee, and picks up shining objects even balls of foil from sweets. Christ obviously knew precisely what was happening, and sent Peter at just the right moment in the life cycle of this fish to fulfil their obligations!]

7. WHALES

The evolution of whales has always been a problem for the evolutionists as they are a sea creature that is nevertheless classified as a mammal because they suckle their young. When Darwin wrote the first edition of his book 'The Origin of Species' in 1859, he had difficulty in explaining how whales could have evolved from a land animal into a sea creature. He assumed that they evolved from land animals as the possiblity of a fish evolving directly into a mammal was too much even for him to accept. He mentioned that bears had been seen swimming in rivers catching fish and suggested that over millions of years they could have gradually evolved so that they developed the fins, tail and other features of whales. How they did this without leaving a single intermediary fossil is a question that never been answered.

In the first edition of his book, Darwin obviously felt that he should put some explanation forward for the evolution of these important and unusual animals. He was well aware how weak his suggestion was, however, for after the first two editions he quietly dropped it from the text.

One would have thought that this whole question of how whales evolved would have been carefully ignored. However, in an issue in

1976 the National Geographic Magazine, throwing caution to the wind, declared that

'The whale's ascendency to sovereign size apparently began 60 million years ago when hairy, four legged mammals, in search of food or sanctuary, ventured into water. As eons passed, changes slowly occurred: hind legs disappeared, front legs changed into flippers, hair gave way to a thick, smooth blanket of blubber, nostrils moved to the top of the head, the tail broadened into flukes and in the bouyant water world the body became enormous [42].'

Once again the imagination is stretched beyond breaking point in order to support the theory of evolution. One cannot but have a degree of admiration for the indominable faith of the evolutionist in his theory in the face of so much opposing evidence!

There is one amusing sidelight on this problem. J.B.S. Haldane was challenged to give a series of aquatic mammals that could have resulted in the whale. He suggested that the sequence could have been; walrus — seal — dugong — whale. This seems at first glance reasonable as there is an increasing tendency to live in the sea. However, it is rather spoiled by the fact that the first two mammals swim by a sideways movement of their tail whilst the latter two use a vertical motion. There would therefore have been some poor animal between the seal and the dugong that had a tail motion at an angle between the two. To say the least, this would have called for an unusual bone structure and made propulsion difficult! [43p22]

8. BLOOD PRECIPITATION TESTS (Immunology)

If small amounts of the clear liquid part of blood, known as the serum, say of a human are injected into a rabbit, the latter will gradually build up anti-human serum. If this anti-serum is then added to the serum of other humans, it will cause a precipitate. By adding this anti-human serum to the blood of various animals and measuring the amount of precipitate resulting, it was claimed that the closeness of the animal to the human species could be assessed. As the results were likely to be supportive of evolution, some 16,000 tests between many different species were carried out by one scientist [17p179ff]

Whilst, as might be expected, there was less reaction from fishes and reptiles to human anti-serum than there was from monkeys, nevertheless, the scatter of results was quite wide. Indeed, the reaction from some monkeys was more than that from some human beings! Many other 'near relationships' could be construed from the various amounts of precipitates, such as the closeness of whales and bats, and that some whales were more nearly related to man than were some monkeys! That these experiments should yield such ridiculous relationships should be sufficient indication that the method is quite worthless. Had the method any real value in classifying species, it would have been greatly developed and further refined. Except for these early experiments, little further work has been done on the method, which is indicative of its value.

Although not referred to much these days, one book does describe the method, but admits 'Immunological evidence is not direct proof of evolutionary relationship, but contributes to the weight of evidence for that view' [37p28]. This seems a reasonable statement, but I will be examining its implications later in section IV.A.2 headed 'Evolutionist's stratagies'.

This immunological evidence for evolution was more often quoted in the past, and it formed an important part of the case of the defence in the famous 'Scopes' trial in America in 1925. In this case, John Scopes was taken to court by creationists for teaching his schoolchildren that man was descended from apes. During the case, the results of these precipitation tests (as well as Java man and Piltdown man) were quoted as 'convincing' evidence for evolution. Yet today they are hardly referred to in view of the wide variation of the values. As we have seen before, evidence such as this seems to be produced at a vital juncture in the course of evolution theory, only to be quietly dropped when the weaknesses are later exposed and admitted.

9. MOLECULAR EVIDENCE

Similar to the technique of blood precipitation tests above, various attempts have been made to find the differing relationships between the species by comparing certain complex chemicals in the body. Amino acid sequences, Cytochrome C and other chemicals have all been investigated to this end, concentrating mainly on trying to discover the relationship between man and the various monkeys. The only trouble with the method however is that it gives different results depending upon which chemical is being considered!

All this is mentioned in the book 'Evolution' by Colin Patterson [11], but there are additional considerations against using chemicals to determine an evolutionary sequence. There are a number of animals that are very 'distant' from humans from an evolutionary point of view, but they have certain complex chemicals that are identical to those in humans. For example, steroid hormones are special biochemical molecules found in man, but are also found in a variety of other animals and even plants, including such 'simple' creatures as sea urchins and starfish [44]. The fact that these animals have this particular type of chemical which does not seem to have evolved to other more complex forms for millions of years is admitted by biochemists to be against the theory of evolution.

Scientists have claimed that by using the rate of mutations in amino acid sequences as a 'molecular clock' they can not only compare the relationships between species (the branching of a phylogenetic tree) but can also obtain some idea of the date when different species diverged. A number of proteins have been investigated and impressive diagrams of the evolutionary sequence have been presented.

The method is not without its critics however, and Scherer [45] has shown that, for both the relationships and the time sequences, it gives results that are very different from the accepted evolutionary scenario. He points out that one worker, in obtaining his impressive results, arbitrarily used 5 million year steps, and only used selected data. When all the available data were used, the rate of the 'clock' was shown to be far from uniform. He quotes another critic as saying 'How sloppy a clock is one prepared to call a clock?' [45p102].

Another work that deals with this subject is 'Evolution: A Theory in Crisis' by Michael Denton [46]. This is an important book for it has been written by a senior scientist who is seemingly not a creationist but who is very critical of the evidence that is used to support evolution. His book covers a wide range of subjects, and should be read by all who are sceptical of both sides of the evoution/ creation divide, for it is objective and thorough in its examination of the facts.

As Denton is a molecular biologist he can speak with some authority on the subject of classification by comparing various chemicals in different species. He comments on this method:

'The really significant finding that comes to light from comparing the protein's amino acid sequence is that it is impossible to arrange them in any sort of evolutionary series ... the whole concept of evolution collapses [because] the pattern of diversity at molecular level conforms to a highly ordered hierarchic system. Each class at a molecular level is unique, isolated and unlinked by intermediaries.' [46p289 and 291]

This is indeed a severe condemnation of even the possiblity of evolutionary links between species.

As with blood tests, these efforts to determine relationships are valueless, but despite this, popular books on evolution will no doubt continue to refer to the methods and quote only those examples that support the theory.

10. GENETIC INHERITANCE

It is usually thought that the genetic information that determines all the features of the offspring is contained in the chromosomes of the parents. Experiments have shown, however, that the cell system as a whole is responsible for heredity and development, which includes both the organelles or internal parts of the cell and the boundary egg-cell membrane (or cortex).

The whole process of how the combined cells of the male and female divide up and eventually produce a complete living organism is phenomenally complex, and scientists have hardly begun to unravel its mysteries. One of the greatest challenges facing geneticists and embryologists is explaining how a particular cell knows what specialised cell it should develop into (bone, muscle etc.). Various theories have been tested but every one has eventually failed.

The subject of inheritance from parts of the cell other than the nuclear genes has received little attention. Indeed, further research in this important subject is not popular or encouraged, and has in fact been actively discouraged in some instances, in precisely the same way that Mendel's papers were deliberately ignored. This is due, no doubt, to the implications it has for limiting any changes in species, for such changes are essential for evolution to proceed.

There is however a group of biologists who are actively engaged in studying this subject for it conforms to their non-Darwinian basic conceptual frameworks (theory or paradigm). These are known as Structuralists, and it will be as well to digress briefly to examine their basic viewpoint.

Structuralism

The basis of the theory of evolution is that 'chance' is the main agent in producing the various organisms that exist today, badly adapted mutations having been eliminated by competition for resources. The Structuralist on the other hand contends that there are certain 'laws' and 'principles' that are the basic forces governing the development of the various forms of life. In order to set out their views, I can do no better than reproduce the contents of a letter I received from Prof. Sermonti of Perugia University (who is the editor of Rivista di Biologia/Biology Forum) with whom I had been corresponding about the Peppered Moth experiments of Kettlewell. Knowing that he was an anti-Darwinist, I wrongly imagined that he was a creationist, and invited him to attend the Fourth European

Creationist Conference to be held at Hagen in Germany in 1990. I
received the following reply.

> 'Dear Mr. Bowden,
> Thank you for your letter of May 18 and your invitation to the
> European Creationist Conference. Although I am a hard anti-
> Darwinian (which jeopardised my career), I would not like to be
> considered Creationist. The main tenet of Structuralism is that
> evolution is not by chance, nor guided by Natural Selection. We
> believe in eternal Rules, in transformation laws, in generating
> principles and sometimes in Archetypes, but we are against
> independant origins, which are implicit in creationism. Similar
> groups however derive from common principles not from common
> ancestors.'
> 'The Osaka group for the Study of Dynamic Structure meets
> once a year ... (summaries have been printed in Rivista di Biologia
> / Biology Forum v80/2 1987 and v82/4 1989) ... We would be
> pleased to receive some consideration from your Movement, with
> which we share the conviction that Darwinism is the worst
> abberation ever occurred in biology. I personally also believe that
> Darwinism is essentially an anti-theistic movement hampering the
> development of biology ... and of civilisation.'
> Yours sincerely,
> Giuseppe Sermonti.'

Clearly, the structuralist is searching for the 'rules', 'laws',
'principles' and 'archetypes' that are the forming agencies for all
organisms. Structuralists are certainly not creationists, and therefore we must ask them the fundamental question 'Where do these
rules and laws originate from?' To this, they either cannot or do not
wish to provide an answer. Sometimes they may claim that this is not
of any immediate importance in their searching. This is surely yet
another example of avoiding the embarrasing conclusions towards
which biological evidence continually points.

We might also suggest why this movement has arisen. Biologists have increasingly come to realise how unproductive and sterile
the theory of evolution is in their sphere of work. The theory relies
upon chance mutations to affect changes, and therefore they are
unable to predict the course of events. Furthermore, there is a
growing body of irrefutable evidence against the theory, which
makes it a difficult position to defend. They have therefore cast
around for an alternative viewpoint, which will allow research to
continue and which will break through the barriers in research —
particularly in genetics — which evolutionists have deliberately
opposed and obstructed for many years.

As they are seeking for rules that exist irrepectively of any God, they might be called modern-day secular Deists. To them the rules exist of their own accord, and not due the activity of a creative God. It is of course possible that they may be aware of the implications of their theory, but having no wish to be tarred with the creationist brush, have opted for a neutral position in order not to lose face with their professional colleagues. They may protest vigorously at this suggestion, but they must accept the criticism in view of their refusal to take their viewpoint to its ultimate conclusion.

Their work is certainly bearing a great deal more fruit than that of staunch evolutionsists, as witnessed by the research into genetics. All such results however can easily be used to support the work of creationists, who have a perfectly satisfactory explanation of the ultimate source of these 'laws'.

It is interesting that one of the members of the Advisory Committee of the periodical Rivista di Biologia/Biology Forum is Professor Brian Goodwin at Milton Keynes. He is leading an active group studying genetic inheritance from a structuralists point of view at the Open University and their views are presented in the Open University Second Level Genetics Course texts.

This newly emerging viewpoint in biology is growing in strength and influence and we are bound to hear more of it. We have therefore digressed at some length in order to be better informed of its theories, the position from which it is coming, and the direction in which it is searching.

11. THE DUCK BILLED PLATYPUS

This unusual animal, illustrated in Fig. 14, presents a major problem to the theory of evolution. When the first stuffed specimens were sent to this country from Australia, for several years they were thought to be a hoax. Such a peculiar combination of features was hard to accept and it was some time before they were taken seriously.

Just consider some of the strange features of the platypus;

a) It has the bill of a duck, but it is soft and very sensitive, for it uses it to forage for food under the surface of the mud. This is necessary as it swims under water with its eyes closed! The bill is so sensitive that it can detect where worms are beneath the mud seemingly by their vibrations, and the minute electrical discharges from their muscles when they move [47]. When burrowing into the earth it can avoid breaking through into other holes made by rats and rabbits etc. again due to its highly sensitive bill detecting their presence.

b) It lays reptilian type eggs similar to those of a turtle, and they are covered with a skin-like texture rather than a hard shell

c) It has fur — so it is not like a duck but more like a mammal. The fur however is waterproof.

d) It suckles its young, but as it has no nipples the milk drips off the hairs of the body which the young lap up.

e) It has webbed and clawed feet that are used for swimming (using the forefeet only) and burrowing. The tough skin on the forefeet can be retracted behind the claws for burrowing and extended beyond them for swimming.

f) It has pockets in its jaws to carry food.

g) It has a shoulder girdle of bones like those of a reptile.

h) It has a flat muscular tail like a beaver's but it is covered with waterproof hairs not scales.

i) In the mating season it has a spur on its rear legs which is poisonous like a snake's fang.

j) It has a highly developed nervous system and a very large brain for its size. The cerebral cortex area of the brain is large which suggests that the animal is very intelligent. It is also exceptionally difficult to rear in captivity, and there are few successes. If their living conditions are not precisely duplicated, they can die in a matter of hours. Indeed, so sensitive is the animal to change that specimens have been known to die in the hands of the captor as they were being taken out of the water.

How such a strange creature could possibly have evolved such a patchwork of contradictory features is a major problem to the theory of evolution. Text books gloss over it by claiming that it is simply a 'transitional stage' between reptiles and mammals, but this is only a cover for avoiding an awkward question. We will therefore leave the subject of this delightful creature, who is quite unaware of the problems his existence has caused, by asking the evolutionists the very simple question — 'What were his ancestors?'

E. INSECT LIFE

There are many thousands of species of insects and some of them have very unusual features. A careful examination of them will often provoke the thought that they simply could not have evolved slowly into the very complex and unusual cratures they are and they must therefore have been designed in accordance with a precon- ceived plan. The parts work together so well that the development of any one section without the other parts also being present would make the whole process or function useless. Thus the concept of

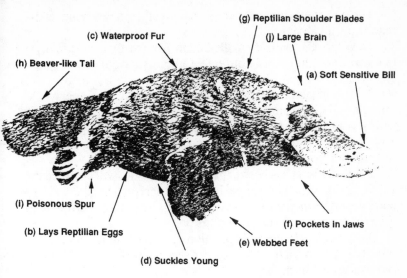

(g) Reptilian Shoulder Blades

(c) Waterproof Fur

(j) Large Brain

(h) Beaver-like Tail

(a) Soft Sensitive Bill

(i) Poisonous Spur

(b) Lays Reptilian Eggs

(f) Pockets in Jaws

(e) Webbed Feet

(d) Suckles Young

Fig. 14. The Duck Billed Platypus

these insects gradually developing to the state that we now find them over millions of years by many small mutations is unacceptable to any thinking person. In this section we will look at a few examples of the way in which some insects have a pattern of behaviour that displays an incredibly complex sequence of events. The reader may like to note other cases that he comes across to add to the list.

1. BOMBARDIER BEETLE

This tiny insect, (Fig. 15A) has an amazing defence mechanism. When attacked, he pumps a mixture of chemicals through two vents at the rear, which react violently and project a jet of hot liquid at an attacker. The beetle has the outlet at the rear end of his body, and is able to aim it in any direction. This hot spray surprises the predator, and while he is recovering from the shock, the beetle has time to scurry away to safety.

The reaction is caused by mixing hydroquinones with a 25% strength hydrogen peroxide, which is strong enough to burn the skin white in a few moments. These chemicals will normally only react at high temperatures, but the beetle also secretes two special enzymes that are extremely complex in both form and operation. One decomposes the peroxide very rapidly without itself being decomposed, whilst the other enzyme catalyses the oxidation of the hydroquinone.

Research [48] has shown just how very sophisticated the jet mechanism really is, and the sequence is illustrated in Fig. 15B.

The two main chemicals are stored together in reservoirs at the rear of the abdomen.

1. When alarmed, a small amount of the two chemicals is pumped through a non-return valve into a strong horny reaction chamber.

2. This chamber secretes the two enzymes, and the whole mixture rapidly explodes. The high pressure generated automatically closes the valve tight, and the jet of liquid at a temperature of 100 degrees Centigrade (the boiling point of water) is propelled through the rear nozzle at the enemy.

3. When the jet has been expelled, the pressure will drop and the valve can then be opened easily. The reservoir chamber pushes another small amount of the two chemicals in and the reaction with the enzymes creates another explosion.

This whole sequence of operations 1-2-3-1-2-3- is very rapidly repeated no less than 500 times per second, and between 2 to 12 pulses may be discharged.

The researchers note that this method of jet emission has many advantages.

i) The high discharge velocity is achieved without using energy in having to contract strong muscles; the explosion provides the force needed.

ii) By not using muscles for the force of the jet, the beetle has better control of the muscles used for directing the jet and it can therefore aim very accurately.

iii) the intermittant flow of cool reactants into the horny reaction chamber helps to lower the temperature and thereby prevent thermal denaturing of the chemicals.

They conclude with an interesting analogy.

'A striking technological analog of the bombadier beetle is provided by the notorious V-1 "buzz" bomb of World War II. Both the beetle and the V-1 engender a pulsed jet through an intermittent chemical reaction, and both have passively oscillating valves controlling access to their reaction chambers. For a propelled vehicle such a system is suboptimal because thrust is discontinuous. For the bombadier beetle the measure is not thrust but rather production of an effective deterrent with good control and high discharge velocity, with investment of minimal muscular force. For this purpose the pulsed mechanism is ideal.' [48p1221]

Again, we seem to have another example of design in nature that is far more efficient than the comparatively clumsy inventions of mankind. It should also be remembered that all these various stages take place in one part of a tiny insect less than 2cm long.

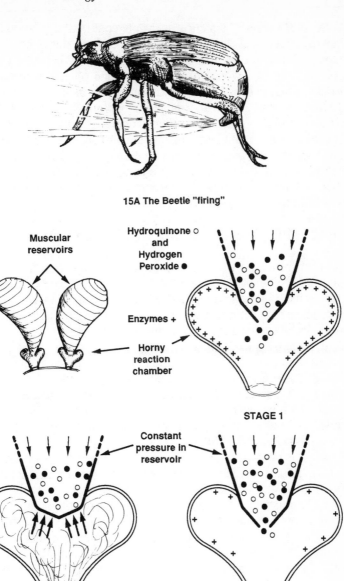

15A The Beetle "firing"

Muscular reservoirs

Hydroquinone ○ and Hydrogen Peroxide ●

Enzymes +

Horny reaction chamber

STAGE 1

Constant pressure in reservoir

STAGE 2

STAGE 3

15B THE PULSING SEQUENCE

Fig. 15. The Bombardier Beetle

Such a complex sequence of events could hardly have taken place by piecemeal development. If a beetle in the remote past 'happened' to make one or more of these chemicals, they might have exploded and that would have been the end of that unfortunate insect, losing the benefit of his 'experiment' for that generation! In addition he would have to arrange his nervous system so that he could control the reaction so that it operated only when it was needed. This and many other factors must be correctly designed to work in the right sequence, otherwise the explosion would either be useless or more likely lethal. There is no satisfactory explanation other than that the bombardier beetle was designed the way it is, right from the very beginning.

2. CATERPILLARS — CHRYSALIDS — BUTTERFLIES

The transformation of an unattractive caterpillar into a delicate butterfly is one of the wonders of nature. The caterpillar first attaches itself by means of a special hook on its tail to a twig. It then proceeds to spin a noose also attached to the twig through which it inserts its head to make itself secure.

It remains quite still and during this chrysalis stage looks lifeless. After many days, from the top of the chrysalis emerges a fully developed butterfly which climbs up the twig. Here it will spread its wings and force into their fine tubular structure a special liquid which will harden in the sun and give them rigidity. It will then fly off and eventually lay eggs that develop into caterpillars to begin another round of the life cycle.

What is perhaps not fully appreciated is the changes that must be taking place inside the chrysalis whilst the caterpiller is being transformed into a butterfly. The caterpiller starts off with heart, stomach, muscles, etc., but all these organs are completely transformed over a period so that the final product is a totally different insect which has delicate wings, changed eyes and many other features. The point is that whilst all this is proceeding, the insect is still a living organism. Amazingly, the whole of the inside of the chrysalis becomes a chemical soup-like material as the various organs dissolve and reform elsewhere as completely different parts of the body of the butterfly! How all this could have come about by small changes over millions of years and what advantage it confers on the insect are difficult problems for evolutionists to explain.

It may be thought that this is a possible mechanism by which new species may have arisen. The changes that occur in the chrysalis stage of the development of the butterfly, however, are so complex

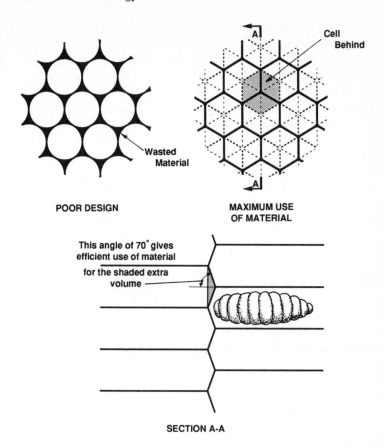

POOR DESIGN **MAXIMUM USE OF MATERIAL**

SECTION A-A

Fig. 16. The honeycomb of the bee

that they must have been carefully designed to take place in a specific sequence. This is quite different to the sudden emergence, by random changes, of a new species from completely different parents as proposed by the 'hopefull monster' theory referred to in section I.F.3. 'Recent Admissions'.

3. THE BEE.

The bee has been the subject of a very great deal of investigation, and consequently, much is knowm about its habits and instincts. Many have seen the various films about this small creature and have been amazed at the superb organisation within the hive. Examples are —

i) Bees that have found a source of food return to the hive and perform a figure of eight 'dance'. The direction of the 'eight' in the

hive indicates the direction of the food and the number of times that
the body vibrates in the figure of eight pattern gives the distance.
The distance is an important factor, for the bees then go to their
supply of food, which is honey, and take just enough of the precious
commodity to enable them to reach the food source and return. If
they misjudge it or are blown off course, they have great difficulty
in returning and often die as they struggle across the surface of the
ground.

ii) They make the familiar six sided walls to the honeycomb to
house their grubs, and it can be proven by advanced differential
calculus that this is one the most efficients shapes for enclosing
space. It uses the minimum amount of material and is very effective
in resisting collapse. At the rear of each cell the walls are shaped to
a point at an angle of 70 degrees to the axis. This gives economic use
of the material in providing the extra volume for this shape (See Fig.
16).

iii) During hot periods the hive is ventilated by some bees
standing on one side of the entrance and vigorously beating their
wings to send air into the hive. On the other side of the entrance,
some face the other way and force air out of the hive.

These are just a few of the fascinating activities of these small
creatures, and much more could be said about the work of the Queen
bee, the many specialised roles of other bees, and their behaviour
when swarming etc. All these and numerous other features are fully
described in the many books on the subject.

4. WASPS

Hunting wasps paralyse caterpillars, or other insects, and lay one
egg on each victim. As the grubs hatch, the caterpillar is the source
of food for the grub. Each species of wasp hunts only one class of
insects. To paralyse a beetle may require only one stab, whilst other
prey may have several separate nerves that require an injection. One
species preys on a caterpillar that has thirteen separate segments and
each one has to be injected at the correct point. To do this so
accurately, the wasp has to have the anatomical ability of a surgeon!
The base of the skull has to be carefully bitten so that the grub is still
living but paralysed.

If the caterpillar becomes too active, it could kill the grub. Two
species of wasp, Odynerus and Eumenes, solve this problem by
hanging an egg from the roof of the cell in which they have deposited
two or three caterpillars. When the egg hatches, the larva hangs
down and nibbles a caterpillar. If it wriggles, the grub simply climbs

up the thread. When it has finished these caterpillars and become stronger, it drops to the floor and eats some 20 other caterpillars that the parent wasp has placed a little further away.

These examples are given to show how difficult it is to explain such behaviour by the theory of evolution. They are a very small sample of many thousands of strange facts in the insect world about which a large book could easily be written.

F. NASCENT ORGANS

If the theory of evolution is true, then it must be asked how certain organs or parts of the body could come into existence. To say that they gradually evolved over a long period raises the problem that most of them would be useless until they were fully developed. According to the theory, the pressure for survival results in ineffi-cient animals being eliminated. If that animal possesses an organ that is only partly developed then it is wasting its energy on something that is as yet useless and should be eliminated. Therefore the pressure is against the survival of any new organs that are developing. Furthermore, the organ may actually reduce the ani-mal's chances of survival such as we have seen in the case of the half developed wings of a reptile that is on its way to evolving into a bird.

The following are just a few examples that have been a subject of debate between evolutionists and creationists.

1. THE EYE

It might be argued that a partially developed organ, such as the eye, may still nevertheless confer some advantage even though it is not fully developed. However, there is a large gap between the small light sensitive areas that some minute animals have and the fully developed eyes that most animals have. It appears perfect and no intermediates are known. As is well appreciated, the human eye is an extremely complex organ for it has —

a) a flexible lens which accurately and automatically focusses upon the curved retina,

b) a retina which is sensitive to colours,

c) the ability to swivel in all directions due to being a sphere,

d) eyelids that keep the suface moist and can blink with amazing rapidity if needed,

e) the iris which automatically adjusts its opening depending upon the amount of light available,

f) ability to estimate distances due to having two eyes, with the ability of the brain to merge the two images into one to give the '3 Dimensional' effect,

g) a small piece of skin in the corner of the eye called the 'semi-lunar fold'.

This last item was claimed to be the 'vestige' of the nictitating membrane, the third eyelid found in some birds and animals, suggesting that we share a common ancestry. However, this fold has a very special purpose and we will digress at this point to show that far from being a vestige, even this small part of the body is beautifully designed.

The following account appears in 'Is Evolution Proved?' [49]. This book, now unfortunately out of print, consists of an exchange of letters between an evolutionist (Shelton) and a creationist (Dewar). In the book, Dewar had pointed out that a publication edited by Julian Huxley and H.G. Wells had referred to this piece of skin as a vestige. In response Shelton proceeded to give the impressive qualifications of the editors in their defence and loftily asked Dewar if he would 'enlighten their ignorance and mine' on the subject. Dewar's reply is as follows.

> 'You ask me to enlighten your ignorance and that of Dr. Julian Huxley and Messrs. H.G. and G.P. Wells as to the use of the semi-lunar fold of the human eye. In the human this fold acts as a scoop which picks up foreign particles that enter the eye, with the result that they become formed into a sticky mass in the corner of the eye where it causes neither irritation or damage and can easily be removed by the finger. The moment a foreign particle gets on to the eyeball the lids close tightly and tears are shed and thus a kind of cistern is formed so that the front of the eye is freely bathed and the offending foreign matter floats in the tears. A special muscle sweeps both tears and foreign matter to the inner corner of the eye and, past the minute orifice of the lachrymal ducts which are raised by the flood of tears from the surface of the eyeball, to the concave membranous edge of the fold which scoops it up and passes it on to the 'caruncula lachrimalis' — a small patch of modified skin covered with fine hairs and provided with sebaceous glands which secrete a fatty substance that envelopes the offending particle.' [49p228]

The eye is most certainly an amazing organ, and when one considers the many features that are listed above, it is surely asking too much to suggest that they just evolved in a random fashion. Indeed, we can understand why Darwin admitted in his 'Origin of Species' in the chapter headed 'Difficulties' that the idea that the eye

' … could have been formed by natural selection, seems, I freely confess, absurd in the highest degree.'

2. THE GIRAFFE'S NECK

One of the most frequent examples that used to be cited as evidence of environment producing change in an animal is the long neck of the giraffe. It was suggested that during times of food shortage, those who had slightly longer necks than average could reach up to the higher branches of trees to eat the leaves and were therefore more likely to survive. Because of this activity their necks became very long over many years. This idea of a small increase in length conferring a distinct advantage was put forward by evolution as evidence in support of theory.

However, the neck of the female giraffe is distinctly shorter than that of the male, whilst that of their young is obviously much shorter still. If a slightly longer neck could result in the survival of a complete species of an animal, then the opposite could also be inferred i.e. during periods of famine, the first to die would be the young and then the females, leaving only the males. In these circumstances, lack of food would not select out the taller males and females but would strike first at the young and then the females. Thus in an area subjected to famine the whole species would be wiped out quite quickly for any remaining males would be unable to reproduce.

Evolutionists now repudiate the examples of the giraffe's long neck, but it still seems to be entrenched in popular thinking. Some simple information about giraffes and a few moments thought is adequate to reveal just how much speculation is involved in evidence of this nature that still occasionaly quoted in support of evolution.

3. JAWS AND EARBONES

The lack of evidence for the evolution of mammals from reptiles has already been considered in the first section. In attempting to describe how this could have taken place some strange transformations have been proposed, one of them being the bones of the jaws and ears of the two groups.

In reptiles the jaws have two bones but a single bone in the ear for transmitting sound. In mammals there is only one jawbone but there are three small bones in the ear. Seeing this, it has been seriously proposed that as the reptile evolved into a mammal these bones changed their function, moving from the jaw to the ear.

Douglas Dewar ridiculed this idea, saying:

' ... some reptile scrapped the original hinge of its lower jaw and replaced it by a new one at a different point. Then some of the bones on each side of the lower jaw broke away from the biggest one. The jaw bone to which the lower jaw on each side was originally attached is supposed to have forced its way into the middle part of the ear, dragging with it three of the lower jaw bones, and these together with the reptile middle ear bone formed themselves into a completely new outfit. [Evolutionists cannot explain] ... how the incipient mammals contrived to eat while the jaw was being rehinged, or to hear while the middle and inner parts of the ear were being rebuilt.' [17p55]

He concluded by saying:

'It is indeed pathetic that educated men should believe that changes such as the above took place in the past by the slow action of natural forces.'

4. 'MOSAIC EVOLUTION'

This is the idea that different parts of an animal have evolved at varying rates. Thus Archaeopteryx was said to be a 'mosaic' combination of bird and reptile features. This term was coined to counter the charge that it was difficult to see how several different parts of an organisation could change at the same time. Darwin claimed that these examples of mosaic evolution showed that different parts could change at different rates. As the parts were still functional, when enough of them had changed, the result would have been a completely different species to the original kind.

This claim however is misleading and completely misses the main problem, for it cannot explain how a complex organ could appear. The eye, for example, could hardly have evolved its various parts at different stages over millions of years; it needs to be fully operational and all the many parts well coordinated to have any real use at all.

Similarly, not only did each of these special features have to be functioning correctly for the animal to use, but each organ had to be fully coordinated with the other organs that (according to the evolutionist) 'belong' to a different class of animal. How these two aspects could be fully complied with so that the animal was still able to survive in the 'struggle for existence' requires yet a further extension of the very elastic credulity of the believer in evolution.

It is to be hoped that the reader's was snapped some pages back!

If a group has a large gene pool that contains a wide range of features, then we might expect some unusual combinations of characteristics to appear in certain local groups that might inter-breed. This is where the difficulties in defining a species arises again. The evolutionist has to recourse to these different 'mosaic' of features arising in separate species from (improbable) chance mu-tations. For the creationist, it is the much wider 'kind' that has to be determined, and this mosaic pattern can be accomodated within this larger range. Alternatively, the creationist has no difficulty in accepting that the Creator designed this specific arrangement of organs for each individual animal.

G. VESTIGIAL ORGANS

Evolutionists quote various examples of organs that appear to have no function and claim these to be the vestiges of organs that were useful at one time but are now 'on their way out'. Indeed, at one time a list of 180 was drawn up, all of them claimed to be vestigial. We have seen above that one of these organs, the semi-lunar fold in the corner of the human eye, far from being a vestige, has an important function. Similarly, the 'vestigial toes' of so-called 'early horses' perform three important tasks in the locomotion of the animals. The discovery of uses for many organs considered to be vestigial continues to grow and the following are two that have been quoted by evolutionists in the past.

i. The bony 'tail' of man is said to be a relic of his ape ancestry. This tail is extended in the human embryo until the later stages when it turns inwards. In this position it serves a useful function in supporting the weight of the intestines and lower organs of the upright human stance.

ii. The male breasts. These are not relics of a man's female ancestry! If this were the case then surely they should have died out during the evolution of our early ancestors. The reason for their existence is that sex characteristics are controlled by hormones. In the early stages of the embryo's progress, the sexual organs for both male and female appear but they are not fully developed and they could become either male or female. The controlling hormones are produced by the male (XY) or female (XX) chromosomes of the embryo depending upon its sex. By the action of the controlling hormones, some of the sexual organs develop in one way, whilst others develop another way or are left undeveloped.

We do not know the use of some organs in animals and man but this does not mean to say that they are quite useless. Some organs may play an important role in the embryo but not after birth. This may well be the case of the human appendix which we consider below.

Having said all this, there nevertheless remain a number of cases where there does seem to be some loss of function. Amongst them are wingless species of insects on windswept islands, blind insects and fish in deep caves and the wings of flightless birds etc. In all these cases it must be noted that there is a *loss* of function, and there are no compensating rudimentary organs that can be shown to be emerging. It therefore seems possible that under certain conditions and probably due to inbreeding within a close knit community, the loss of a function may cause no serious impairment of the creature. In this case it is able to survive and pass this loss of a function on to its offspring. This gives little support to the theory of evolution however, for it must provide not simply a loss of function but more important, some mechanism for generating new organs, and this it is quite unable to do.

THE HUMAN APPENDIX

This is one of the most frequently quoted examples of a 'vestigial' organ that it deserves special consideration. Because it can be removed from humans without ill effect it is immediately classed as vestigial. Yet the following points should be considered.

i. The fact that it can be removed does not mean that it has no use whatsoever. It is quite likely that its function is also carried out by other organs that can adequately perform the same role. By illustration, a person's little finger could be severed but he does not die. Yet no one would think of calling it 'vestigial'.

ii. The appendix is situated at the junction of the small bowel and the large bowel and may be used to resist bacterial infection. Its role may be similar to that of the tonsils in the throat. It also produces a lubricating mucus, and patients that have had their appendix removed can suffer from constipation.

iii. It is particularly rich in lymphatic tissue, a feature that it shares with the thymus gland. The thymus is particularly important in the functions of the body for it enables a body to recognise its own flesh. In the new born animal, the thymus is quite large and if removed immediately after birth, the animal is unable to discern whether a graft is from itself or not and therefore accepts it. This may seem to be an advantage but the problem is that it is also unable to recognise invading bodies and can die as a result of infection as it cannot recognise the invaders as being hostile. It is for this reason that heart transplant patients have to have to be treated to temporarily neutralise the body's defence mechanism so that it does not reject the new heart. If the thymus is left in for several days after birth, then the body learns to recognise its own cells and reject those which are alien. There is a link between the thymus and the appendix in the immunological system, for the thymus produces 'T' cells whilst the appendix produces similar "B" cells. Their whole complex operation is not fully understood, but there are more incidents of bowel cancer and infection if the appendix is removed.

The thymus has been examined in some detail as this organ was also one of the many that featured on the list of 180 'vestigial' organs that have since been shown to have an important function. The lymphatic sytem of the human body is large, and whilst parts of it, such as the appendix, may be dispensed with, this does not mean that these organs are useless.

iv) The appendix is the subject of a classic case of evolutionary interpretation and separate contradiction within just one publication — Gray's Anatomy (36th edition 1980). Glover [50] notes that it 'indicates in its embryology section that the appendix is a vestigial remnant indicative of man's ancestors' more herbivorous dietary habits, whereas the anatomical section says "In view of its rich blood supply and histological differentiation, the vermiform appendix is probably more correctly regarded as a specialised than as a degenerate vestigial structure"'. Glover comments 'Surely one can't have it both ways!'

H. INSTINCTS

Many animals clearly demonstrate that much of their activity is carried out by instincts that are built into their genetic information. We have already mentioned some of the behaviour patterns of insects and others will be given in the part following, which deals with plant fertilisation.

A surprising number of animals are known to migrate, including eels, salmon, elephants, bats, turtles, plankton and whales, in varying degrees. The migration of eels from the rivers of Europe to their spawning grounds amongst the seaweed of the Sargasso Sea near the West Indies, is well known. Other examples could also be given in detail. In this section we will concentrate on two aspects of bird behaviour — their migration and nesting habits.

1. MIGRATION

The immense distances travelled by birds when migrating is a well known fact. Many thousands of birds have been ringed in order to determine their route and how far they migrate, whilst experiments have been made to discover what navigational methods are used.

When the small size of many of the birds is considered, the distances they travel are even more amazing. The following is a list of a few that travel great distances and some routes are shown in Fig. 17.

Artic Tern N.	Canada	Antartica	14,000 miles
Wilson's Petrel	Antartica	North Atlantic	9,000
Barn Swallow N. Canada	N. Central Argentina		9,000
White Stork	Germany S. Africa		8,000
Golden Plover N˙ Canada	Argentina		8,000
Great Shearwater Tristan da Cuhna	N. Atlantic		7,000

The Great Shearwater leaves the island of Tristan da Cuhna, flies to the North Atlantic and then finds its way back to this tiny dot of an island in the middle of the vast ocean of the South Atlantic. This is an amazing feat of navigation as well as that of endurance.

THE GOLDEN PLOVER

The time when the Golden Plover migrates is a problem for evolutionists. It rears its young during the harsh winter season of Northern Canada. Then, just as the warmer weather is arriving, it flies out across Labrador, bypasses the United States, goes down the Eastern side of the Atlantic and crosses back to reach Brazil and Argentina. The return trip is by quite a different route. They first cross the Andes and then fly over the Panama Canal, then up the Mississippi River to their starting point in the bitterly cold land on the edge of the Antarctic continent. Why should these birds leave their northern home just when the available food is most abundant? This and many other similar questions remain unanswered.

There is one fascinating feature that has been discovered [51] in the migration of the Golden Plover which probably applies to the majority of other migratory birds. Some Plovers fly non stop from Alaska direct to Hawaii over the sea, a distance of 4,000 kilometers (2,500 miles). It takes 88 hours of flying (during which each bird

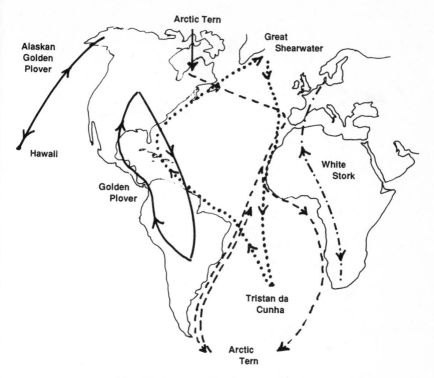

Fig. 17. Routes of migratory birds

makes 250,000 wing beats). It starts with a body weight of 200 grams of which 70 grams is fat that is used as fuel in flight. For every hour it flies it is known to consume 0.6% of its body weight in fat. As it uses up the fat it gets lighter and therefore uses slightly less fat each hour. Calculations show that it would use 82 grams of fat in 88 hours which is greater than its resource of 70 grams and therefore it should fall exhausted into the sea before it gets to Hawaii. Yet they do reach their destination. How do they do it?

The secret is that the bird has an important piece of information to help it. This is that flying in formation uses 22% less fuel than if they were flying alone! The turbulence created by the lead bird is used by the following bird whose turbulence in turn is used by the third bird and so on. By flying at a specific distance and position from the bird in front where his turbulence gives them this extra lift, they can conserve their energy. This is why they fly in echelon formation when on long flights, the birds taking it in turn to be in the lead (Fig 18). When this flying efficiency factor is included within the calculations, it can be shown that after 88 hours, they arrive at their destination with a small reserve of fat! (Fig. 19)

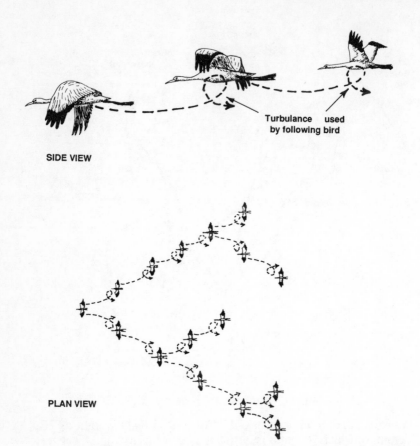

SIDE VIEW

Turbulance   used
by following bird

PLAN VIEW

Fig. 18 Efficiency of echelon formation of bird flight.

Could the birds have possibly learnt this fact after much trial and error over many generations or was it implanted within them by their Creator?

The furthest known migration is that of the Arctic Terns, and here again, the route that they take is unusual. Most of them nest in Northern Canada but some are as far south as Cape Cod near Boston. These more southern based Terns fly straight across the Atlantic to just off Spain, then follow the west coast of Africa, cross the Atlantic again to the southern tip of South America and then down to Antarctica. Some birds fly a round trip of a staggering 14,000 miles!

NAVIGATION

Scientists have tried to discover how birds can navigate so accu-

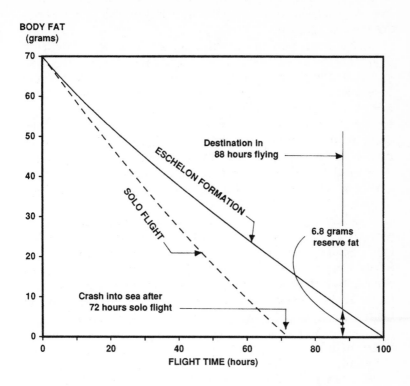

Fig. 19. Energy consumption of the Golden Plover

rately. They have found that they use the stars, the sun and the earth's magnetic field [52], to achieve their pin point accuracy. It is also thought that they can hear the noise of waves breaking on the shore as a further guide. Their ability to use the earth's magnetic field is due to sensitive crystals in the nose, and strangely, some humans have a similar ability to sense direction.

Birds have been set free over the open sea up to 1368 kilometres (820 miles) from their small island home, to which they eventually returned. Other birds have been drugged or their cages continuously turned so that they were completely disorientated, but they still found their way home. The conclusion was that they must possess a real sense of geographical position. i.e. they know precisely where they are on the globe, and which direction to fly to reach their nests. How this is done completely baffles those who have spent years experimenting in the subject.

All these abilities are known to be quite instinctive and already built into the minute brain of these small creatures. The problem is how did it get there in the first place. Some fascinating experiments have been carried out showing that the navigational information is genetically inherited.

It has been noticed that caged migratory birds hop and flutter in their cages in the direction that they would have taken had they been free, even changing the direction at the precise time that they would have done so in navigating in the wild. There are two closely related European blackcap warblers: The German warbler travels south-west to avoid the Alps, whilst the Austrian warbler avoids them by going southeast. When crossbred, the offspring appear to inherit part of the 'navigational map' from each parent, for they take a direction due south. This would lead them directly over the Alps on a path on which they would certainly perish [Behavioral Ecology and Social Biology 1991 v28 p9-12].

If this migratory information is genetically inherited, then this presents a problem for evolutionists. The information for under-taking any long and dangerous journey has to be correct for any error would result in the death of the bird. Changing any such instructions genetically by numerously small stages by mutations could not have produced the necessary information correctly at all stages; like so many other features in nature, it has to be 'right first time'.

Scientist admit that they cannot explain of how such a strange pattern of behaviour as migration could have arisen either by chance or by conferring any beneficial effects that would have given them an advantage in the 'struggle for survival'. To undertake journeys of such enormous distances can hardly be said to give migrating birds any greater ability to survive. Such seemingly unnecessary and strenuous journeys must take their toll of the population and consume a great deal of energy; energy that could be put to better use if there is any such life-or-death 'struggle for survival' as required by the theory of evolution. It need hardly be said that those birds that do not migrate still nevertheless survive quite successfully.

In considering the problem of migration, there seems to be only one reasonable solution. The necessary instructions and naviga-tional abilities could only have been carefully planned and im-planted in the birds by a Master Planner.

2. NESTING HABITS

There is a wide variety of nests made by birds, from a scrape in the ground to very elaborate constructions. Douglas Dewar was a keen ornithologist in India, and for many years accepted the theory of

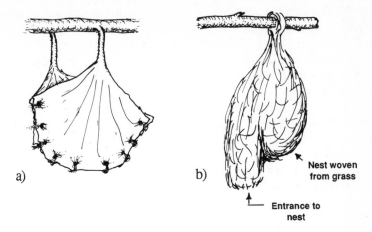

Fig. 20. The nests of A) a Tailor bird.   B) a Weaver bird.

evolution uncritically. It was not until he studied the nests of some of the native birds that he realised that they could not possibly have been constructed by a gradual increase in experience over many generations. Some constructions had to be correctly made the very first time or they would be quite useless for their purpose of raising their young.

One of the birds that made him realise this was the Tailor bird. This bird has a most unusual nest for it actually sews together the opposite edges of a leaf (Fig. 20A). It punches a series of holes down each edge and pulls them together with strands of cobwebs. These are then reinforced with cotton fibres that are tied in a knot. The inside is then lined with more cotton to form the nest. If the stitching is badly made, as it would be on the first attempt, then the eggs would fall, the brood would be destroyed and the experience that might have been gained would not therefore be passed on to their off-spring.

Another bird that intrigued Dewar was the Weaver bird. The male tears thin strips from the coarse grasses, binds them around a branch and weaves more grass strips from them to form a rope about four inches long. This is then expanded into a bell shape, across the bottom of which a loop is plaited. Using the loop as a platform, he weaves a hanging basket shape. The entrance to this is then con-structed in the form of a woven tube leading to the top of the nest, so that the final shape of the whole nest is like a chemist's retort (Fig. 20B).

Such complicated constructions as these birds make are far too difficult for them to have arisen by a slow learning process over succeeding generations.

We do not have to go to India however for a demonstration of the intricacy of nest building. Our own House Martin's nest of mud is very carefully made. Each morning, the bird gets some wet mud from a nearby stream, and mixing it with some saliva, forms the first part of the nest on the wall of a building. It then waits during the afternoon to allow it to dry thoroughly and harden. The following morning it repeats the process, adding a further layer, until after several days the nest is complete. If it did not ensure that the mud was correctly mixed and dry enough, the nest would fail when the eggs were laid.

Thus, even such small objects as birds' nests refute the theory of evolution.

I. PLANTS

Although it receives much less attention than animals in textbooks, plant life demonstrates some very unusual patterns of behaviour and cooperation with animals and insects. This is particularly so with regard to the many different ways by which plants achieve cross fertilisation with other plants, even though they cannot move themselves. Some of the more interesting ways are given here.

1. THE BUCKET ORCHID.

This plant must surely have the most incredible of all the various methods of fertilisation. It was first brought to the public's attention in a television broadcast entitled 'Sexual Encounters of the Floral Kind' in the series of 'The World About Us' in September 1981. The sequence of events can be followed in Fig. 21.

The male orchid bee (1) gathers from the surface of the flower of the orchid a liquid that makes him attractive to the female bee. The sides of the flower are slippery and sometimes a bee falls into the bucket (2). In the bottom of the bucket is a pool of liquid that collects there as it drips from a gland above. The unfortunate bee can only escape one way and that is by a tunnel out of the side of the bucket. There is a convenient step (3) to enable the bee to reach the lower end of the tunnel, but when it is just about to emerge, the small hole (4) through which it has to pass suddenly contracts and holds the bee for a short time.

While it holds the bee in this position, the plant puts two pollen sacs on its back and secures them with some glue, holding the bee until the glue has set. When the bee's body is dry of the liquid, it flies off to other bucket orchids (5). Some of the bees with pollen sacs fall

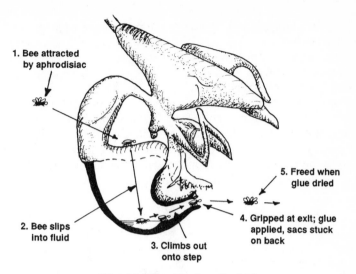

1. Bee attracted by aphrodisiac

5. Freed when glue dried

2. Bee slips into fluid

4. Gripped at exit; glue applied, sacs stuck on back

3. Climbs out onto step

Fig. 21. The Bucket Orchid.

into the bucket of a different plant. As they emerge from the tunnel, at the point where it was firmly gripped before, a special hook protruding from the roof of the tunnel neatly picks the two bags from its back!

In such an amazing way is this plant fertilised. How could such a series have arisen by chance? It requires only one of the many stages in the complex sequence to be imperfectly developed for the whole fertilisation method to fail completely and the bucket orchid would cease to be. The mere fact that it exists is adequate proof that it was designed to operate in the form we have it today.

2. BEE POLLINATION

The hive bee is perfectly designed not only for the gathering of honey but for the pollination of the particular species of plant that it is visiting that day. As it thrusts its tongue into the flower to gather the nectar, its antennae become covered in pollen. This is scraped off by using a special notch in the foreleg, and the foreleg is then scraped by the middle which is in turn scraped by the hind leg which is provided with a rake in one of the joints. When the joint is closed, the pollen is packed into a compact mass and held in position by a special spike on the leg for this purpose. When collecting nectar, hive bees visit only one species of plant during any particular period, thus ensuring that the cross pollination is most efficient.

3. THE ARUM PLANTS.

During the night, the plant opens and begins to emit a carrion smell. In the morning, tiny flies are attracted by the smell. These land on the flower and they push into the flower chamber past a ring of hairs that prevents them from escaping again (Fig. 22). They may have the pollen from another plant on them, and in their attempts to escape, they will brush some off onto the stigmas of the female flowers, thus fertilising them and preventing self fertilisation. By the following night, the plant has produced its own pollen and the insect becomes covered by it. On the next morning, the trap hairs shrivel, the smooth sides of the spathe become roughened and the insect, covered with new pollen, escapes to fertilise another plant.

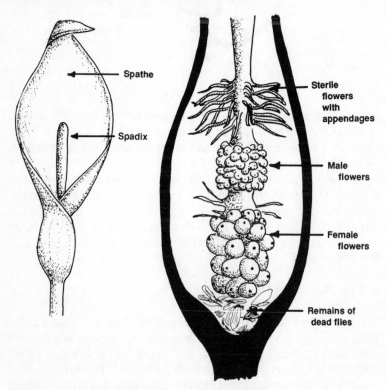

Fig. 22. The Arum plant

4. SALVIA.

This uses a most ingenious lever system for pollination. As the insect moves into the flower, it pushes against the lower end of the anther which acts like a pivoted lever, and the outer end swings downward and places the pollen on the back of the insect (Fig. 23). In the younger plants with mature pollen, the style stays up clear of the insect so that it does not collect its own pollen off the insect. As the plant matures, the anther withers but the style curls over so that it is at the same point where the anther would have touched the bee. When the bee arrives from another Salvia that has only the anthers with pollen operating, the style rubs the pollen off the insects back, thus achieving cross fertilisation.

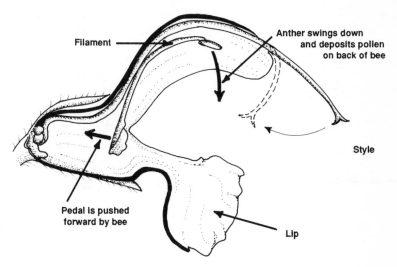

Fig. 23. The Salvia flower.

Many other strange methods of pollination could be given, but sufficient has been said to show that even in the minute world of plants and insects, there is much evidence of design even in the smallest detail.

J. SUMMARY OF BIOLOGICAL EVIDENCE

As Darwin admitted that the geological evidence was actually against evolution, he carefully selected suitable examples from the phenomenally varied field of biology to provide the evidence he needed to support his theory. However, as we have tried to show above, careful examination of every single example that we have examined can to be shown to be not simply inadequate as proof of the theory but actually against it.

It is surely obvious to anyone prepared to look at the evidence from a reasonably unbiassed point of view (if that is at all possible) that it simply shouts at you that the wonderful world in which we live did not arise by chance but must have been designed. Furthermore its Designer must have possessed infinite wisdom to have conceived the variety of beautiful and intricate forms of life that we have today.

SECTION III — PHYSICS

A. THE CHEMICAL PRODUCTION OF 'LIFE'

Evolutionists have considerable difficulty in explaining how life could have started by the chance combinations of elements. The theory proposed is that simple gases were in the atmosphere when the earth was cooling down after its first formation. Discharges of lightning through them produced a number of different chemicals that became more and more concentrated in the sea so that it became a 'primeval soup'. In this mixture, complex compounds gradually combined together to form active life and eventually a 'simple' cell.

1. MILLER'S EXPERIMENT

In 1952, Miller passed a mixture of the gases methane, ammonia and hydrogen through a spark and drew off the resulting compounds (Fig. 24). When he analysed them he found that there was a small quantity of amino acids. Amino acids are what might be called the basic building blocks of life for they occur in various combinations to form many of the complex chemicals found in living tissue. This production of amino acids in the laboratory prompted world wide publicity in which claims were made that 'life had been created in the laboratory'. Such claims however were greatly exaggerated and the following criticisms of this experiment will show how unlikely the possibility of creating life in the laboratory really is.

    i) The mixture of gases Miller used is one that scientists have assumed existed at the beginning of the earth's history. One of the difficulties facing them is that the present atmosphere contains free oxygen which would have immediately combined with the amino acids making them useless. It therefore needed a 'reducing' atmosphere and this was provided by carefully selecting the mixture of gases in the experiment. Of course, the scientists then have to explain how the atmosphere later changed to the oxidising one we have today without affecting the life forms that had evolved in a reducing atmosphere — but that, as they say, 'is another story'!

    ii) The heat from a spark and the ultra-violet light will both

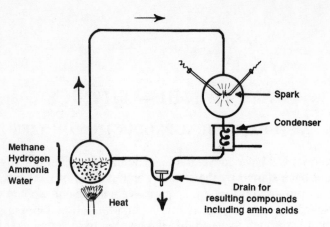

Methane
Hydrogen
Ammonia
Water

Spark

Condenser

Drain for
resulting compounds
including amino acids

Heat

Fig. 24. Miller's experiment.

quickly destroy the amino acids and they therefore have to be removed immediately from the spark and separated out by the trap. How such a separation could have occurred in nature is difficult to imagine. Furthermore, the compounds themselves slowly break up of their own accord. This is because they require energy to form them and this 'locked up' energy gradually breaks them down. The result is that only a *very* minute amount could possibly have entered into the sea, and even then the ultra-violet light would have continued to break them down whilst they were in the first few metres of depth. The total volume of the sea is some 320 million cubic miles and the concentration of these amino acids would have been so low that there would have been really no possibility of any chemical combinations occurring.

2. MATHEMATICAL IMPOSSIBILITY

It can be shown that the chances of life evolving from the elements is a mathematical impossibility in view of the very specialised products that are required compared with the great number of possible (useless) combinations that could have formed by chance.

Amino acids are used in the formation of proteins and DNA and other organic compounds. There are twenty different amino acids, but each one can be either 'right handed' or 'left handed' depending upon how the atoms are related to each other. The right handed ones are useless for the forming of organic compounds which only leaves the left handed ones that can be utilised. In what follows however we will ignore this and simply assume that there are twenty amino acids to choose from and not a total of forty. Even with this reduction, the chances against life starting are astronomic.

Proteins consist of a very long chain of amino acids, some of them consisting of several thousand units. In order to demonstrate the impossibility of life arising by chance combinations of chemicals we will consider a small proteinoid made up of only 100 amino acids. In all organic compounds the sequence of each of the amino acids has to be precisely correct order otherwise the compound is useless. What are the chances of these chemicals coming together to form a particular proteinoid only 100 units long?

Obviously, the chance of the first one being correct is one chance in 20. The chance of two of them being correct is 1 chance in $20 \times 20 = 400$. Similarly for the third position also to be filled with the correct amino acid, it is 1 in $20 \times 20 \times 20 = 8000$. For all one hundred positions to be correctly filled the chances are 1 in 20^{100} (one hundred twenties all multiplied together). This number is roughly equal to 10^{130} (1 with 130 noughts behind it) — an enormously large number that is far greater than the total number of atoms (10^{80}) that one expert has calculated that there are in the whole known universe.

To give another example, the protein Insulin has 51 amino acids in a specific sequence. The chance against this forming is 1 to (3 with 68 noughts after it). If all possible combinations of 51 amino acids were tried at a rate of one billion per second, it would still take 10^{52} *years* to produce one correct sequence that would be Insulin. It can now be manufactured in the laboratory, but it requires no less than 5,000 separate and quite difficult operations to produce just a small quantity. In the cell it takes only about 1 minute!

With the chances against the formation of even a small protein being so large, it is clear that the possibility of life starting from simple chemicals combining together in the 'primeval soup', or in any other way, simply could not have taken place. The odds against it are far too great. Further evidence showing that evolution cannot even clear this first hurdle is presented in a number of books, one of the best being reference 53.

Richard Dawkins' 'The blind watchmaker'

Paley, in his 'Natural Theology', published in 1802, claimed that if we were to find a watch in a field, then in view of its intricate design, we would deduce that there must be a watchmaker. In the same way, we can deduce that there must be a creator/designer when we examine the phenomenal intricacy in the natural world. This has been, and still is, one of the simplest and most powerful arguments against evolution, and therefore Dawkins uses every method he can to overcome it by claiming that the 'watchmaker' is Natural Selection that works 'blindly' through chance — hence the title of his book.

Dawkins agrees (with creationists) that if all the possible permutations have to be tried as single steps in composing a complex chemical like a protein, then the number becomes impossibly large. What he then does is to create his own terminology — 'cumulative selection' — which he defines as follows;

> 'In single-step selection the entities selected or sorted, pebbles or whatever they are, are sorted once and for all. In cumulative selection, on the other hand, they "reproduce"; *or in some other way* the results of one sieving process are fed into subsequent sieving, which is fed into ... , and so on. The entities are subjected to selection of sorting over many "generations" in succession. The end-product of one generation of selection is the starting point for the next generation of selection, and so on for many generations. It is natural to borrow such words as "reproduce" and "generation", which have association with living things, because living things are the main examples of things that participate in cumulative selection. They may in practice be the only things that do. But for the moment I don't want to beg that question by saying so outright.' (p45).

This is an important passage, for on it he bases much that follows in the book. His precise meaning however is far from clear.

Dawkins gives an example (p47) of a random set of 28 letters which are changed randomly, those tries which are 'nearest' to the desired (predetermined) result are used as the basis for a further set of tries. The complete phrase ('Methinks it is like a weasel') is achieved within only 43 to 64 stages by a computer, the precise number depending upon the particular random selection of letters started with. This may seems persuasive to some, but there are serious flaws in his reasoning.

i) He has already decided in this programme the number of units he is working towards. Yet he maintains that evolution is 'blind', in that it does not know what the future coding might be best. i.e., the length might need to change for a particular stage of the evolution of a chemical. This presents a totally unknown quantity in the programming of the computer.

ii) He does not say what one 'stage' (generation) consists of in his computer programme. If, as referred to above, only *one* unit is changed at a time, then he should get about the same order of astronomical odds as would the single-step method. It would appear that his programme produces numerous random changes ('mutations') in those units that are different from the target sentence. From these, one 'winning phrase' is selected that is 'nearest' to it. This is called "one generation", and this is then subjected to further changes *only of those units that still differ from the target phrase* , and so on for as many generation as are needed to reproduce the target.

He does not say how many variations (mutations) each generation is able to choose from. If there are millions of them, then there is much more likelihood that more units match the target. This would greatly reduce the number of generations that are needed. His failure to give the number of mutations available for selection makes the low value of generations he needed for a correct answer quite meaningless.

iii) He notes that in single-step selection, the entities 'are sorted once and for all'. In cumulative selection it would seem that those units that already have the correct letter are also 'fixed once and for all', just as in the single-step method. But if mutations are really pure chance and can make changes in both the letters *and the positions it makes the change*, then the correct 'fixed letters' can also be changed, and the odds become as astronomical as for the single-step method. The prevention of any changes in correct letters means that the method is no longer random.

iv) As we have noted in the section on the chemical composition of a protein, it requires in some of them only one amino acid to be incorrect and the protein will be useless. Thus, any scenario that requires a random selection of units simply cannot have any possible use during any of the intermediate stages. It could not function and would be rejected.

v) The most obvious objection to his very simplistic example is that he has already determined what the final phrase is to be. If he tries to apply this to 'blind' mutations, then they must 'know' what they are 'aiming at', both in exact length and order of amino acids (letters). But this he must reject in his evolutionary philosophy, for then his 'watchmaker' is no longer blind! His various examples therefore contradict his basic contention.

In a later example, he uses a computer again to generate lines on a screen, using a similar type of programme. He graphically describes his astonishment at the resulting forms that appeared when he chose different paths for the computer to follow. He labelled these members of 'biomorph land' with titles such as 'scorpion', 'caddis', 'tree frog', 'crossed swords' etc. but again, they are only lines on a screen. It is his human mind that gives them these very suggestive titles. Granted that he refers to this aspect, but once again, there is the implication that if this can be done in a matter of seconds by a computer, then given enough time, nature can achieve similar results in living organisms. This is of course precisely the same 'leap of faith' that Darwin had to propose in order to have a mechanism through which evolution could take place.

This book is often quoted as answering the creationist's claims particularly regarding the seeming design in nature, but as we have seen, the logical foundation is badly flawed. In Appendix 4 I will be examining Dawkin's deliberate use of 'tricks of the advocates trade' in his presentation of the evidence.

3. THE INFORMATION PROBLEM

One of the major problems facing evolutionists is the source of the very specific sequence of chemical molecules that must be followed in the production of a useful compound. This problem of information (as against randomness) will be referred to in different ways in other sections; e.g. Entropy

The sequence of the amino acids in a protein is clearly important, but biochemists have not reached the stage where the code can be followed from source to its final production of a specific chemical, organ or activity. Although the way in which it operates may not be known, that the sequence has information is certain, for changing one amino base can ruin the effectiveness of the protein.

The sequence is very similar to the letters on a page of typing. A monkey could tap randomly but never produce a whole sentence that had meaning. We are able to transfer information by means of letters because there are particular patterns of letters that have been agreed by the laws of the language to convey a specific meaning to the person reading them. For example the word 'cat' is three simple letters, and informs the reader that a particular animal is being referred to. The sequence 'tac' in English has no meaning but the letters are the same. Similarly, the fact that there is actual information contained within the sequence of the amino acids that the other chemicals can act upon is an important feature of all cell activity.

Within the cell, there is the additional problem of the difference between the enzymes (functioning proteins) and the nucleic acids (RNA and DNA — information proteins). The enzymes carry out the instructions given by the RNA and DNA. Each of them depends upon the other, for the enzymes need the information in the nucleic acid chain, whilst they in turn need the enzymes to carry out the instructions. Thus each is necessary, and on their own they cannot function at all.

Whilst considering this question of information contained

within the chromosomes, there is one function of the sequence of the chemicals where the scientists have little knowledge, that we have touched on before. This is the way in which information contained in the genes is actually converted to produce the characteristic they control. Their ignorance of how this information results in specific features in the embryo and the developed organism is not so much a gap but more like an unbridged chasm.

4. COMPLEXITY OF A 'SIMPLE' CELL

In describing the progress of evolution it is sometimes referred to as tracing the path 'from ameoba to man' and the phrase often used is that 'complex chemicals collected together to form a simple cell'. Thus the impression is given that such a cell is a gathering together of a few chemicals that fortunately had the ability to work together and moreover could reproduce themselves. The gross oversimplification of this picture becomes evident when a cell is examined and its phenomenal complexity is revealed. I give a section of a typical cell in Fig. 25 and even this is greatly simplified.

Biochemists have taken many years to unravel some of this information which is only a very small part of the whole interconnecting network of events. The following features will give some idea of how complex the picture is in practice.

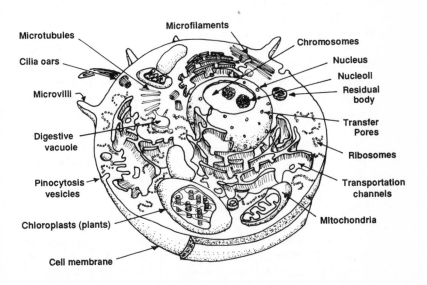

Fig. 25. The parts of a cell

i) *The cell wall* is permeable to some chemicals but not to others, and the permeability can be changed continuously. Furthermore, it has been found that it contains genetic information as we have considered in section II D 10.

ii) *Mitochrondria* are the centres where energy is produced for the various functions of the cell.

iii) *The Endoplasmic reticulum* (with attached ribosomes) is the area in which the cell fabricates its proteins, fitting the right amino acids together in the correct sequence rather like a zip runner clips together the two halves of the zip. One half has the master pattern and the other half fits into it accordingly and then separates with the amino acids in their correct order.

iv) *Enzymes*. In order to make some chemicals react with one another they often have to be heated up. If this was the process used by the cells of the body they would be destroyed by the heat long before some important chemical reactions could have taken place. How does the cell overcome this problem? It does it by special chemicals known as enzymes. These are the vitally important chemicals that attach themselves to the two chemicals which then combine easily together. The reaction takes place at a low temperature and very efficiently. The enzyme then separates itself from the resulting product so that it is free to engage two more chemicals.

One enzyme can process billions of reactions every second which gives you some idea of their efficiency. There are about three thousand enzymes in an average body cell and each one is designed for use in a specific type of reaction.

v) *The nucleus* contains the chromosomes which consist of long chains of a chemical known as DNA (deoxyribonucleic acid). These contain the 'blueprint' for replication of the cell so that the resultant daughter cells contain the same information for their activity and further replication as the parent cell. The DNA also codes for the enzymes that control all the chemical reactions in the cell.

These are just some of the reactions that have been found to take place in a living cell — a tiny unit which is far too small to be seen with the naked eye.

5. EVOLUTIONIST'S ADMISSIONS

The inability of biologists to discover precisely how a cell operates and reproduces itself is one of the major stumbling blocks of evolution. Many of the workers in this field admit that they are a long way from understanding the phenomenally complex interactions within the cell and two of them have said:

'The molecule-to-cell transition is a jump of fantastic dimensions which lies beyond the range of testable hypothesis. In this area all is conjecture. The available facts do not provide a basis for postulating that cells arose on this planet' [54]

It is recorded that Prof. J.B.S. Haldane was prepared to debate the issue of evolution with creationists, provided that the question of the origin of life was excluded. This not only indicates how inadequate the theory is to explain the existence of life but that supporters of the theory are well aware of this fact.

6. LIFE FROM OUTER SPACE?

Aware that it is virtually impossible to show even in theory that life could have developed on this earth, evolutionists have therefore suggested that it may have originated somewhere in space.

The latest efforts in this line are by Professors Hoyle and Wickramasinghe. Having shown the mathematical impossibility of life forming upon this planet, they have proposed that it has come via meteorites from outer space, pointing to the outbreak of world wide virus infections after periodic showers of meteorites. Their claims have been disputed and even more importantly, they admit that there is just as much difficulty facing the formation of life out there as there is on this earth [55p31].

There have been several attempts to show that some form of organic material may have been brought to this earth by meteorites. Sometimes tests on them have shown the presence of bacteria, which seems to supports this case. Stringent precautions have been taken to ensure that they were not contaminated during the handling process of obtaining them from the ground, and it was therefore concluded that they must have come from outer space.

There were, however, counterarguments, the most damaging being those of one researcher who proved that rocks as solid as basalt would become contaminated by bacteria even within their interior if the rock remained buried in soil [53p109]. With the enormous heat generated by the entry into the earth's atmosphere, there would be numerous cracks opening up that would assist the bacteria to permeate a meteorite. Furthermore, microfossils could have been washed into the interior by permeating ground water.

There have also been found in meteorites some organic chemicals, including amino acids, together with a chemical similar to the hard material around spore pollens. Discovery of these was claimed as evidence that there was life in outer space. Croft, however, explains their presence as being due to the meteorite absorbing in its cracked surface some of the immense amount of pollen that there is in the atmosphere. These are decomposed during the descent which produces the slightly changed organic chemicals that are detected. He points out that several of the chemicals are also found in honey which is made from pollen, and therefore there is good evidence that pollen contamination is a reasonable explanation. He also notes that if indeed meteorites do contain organic material, this should also be found on our moon, but very sensitive tests on its surface have completely failed to detect anything [53p111].

B. RADIOMETRIC DATING OF ROCKS

1. THE METHOD

There are two main types of strata — the sedimentary layers that consist of clays, sands and gravels etc. that have been laid down under water, and the igneous rocks that have come up from the hot interior of the earth and spread out between the sedimentary layers or over the surface and then cooled. These igneous rocks usually contain a very small amount of radioactive elements such as Uranium 238, Uranium 235, Thorium, Rubidium and Potassium 40. Each of these elements is unstable and radioactively decays into a 'daughter' product very slowly over a long period of time.

The rate at which they decay is measured by their 'half lives'. This is the time taken for any particular amount of the element to decay to half of its weight. For example, the half life of Uranium 238 is 4,510 million years. If you have say 16 grams of Uranium now, then in 4,510 million years time you would have 8 grams of uranium and the equivalent of 8 grams of the daughter product (Lead 206), that it decays into. In a further 4,510 million years time you would have 4 grams of Uranium and 12 grams of Lead, and as further time went by, the Uranium would decrease slowly and the Lead increase (Fig. 26).

It is assumed by geologists (and it is a very big assumption) that when the igneous rock came up to the earth's surface, it contained only the radioactive element and none of the daughter element. Then, as the radioactive material decayed and decreased, the amount of the daughter element gradually increased.

By simply measuring the amount of radioactive material and comparing it with the amount of the daughter element present in the rock, the scientists claim that they can date the age of the rock when

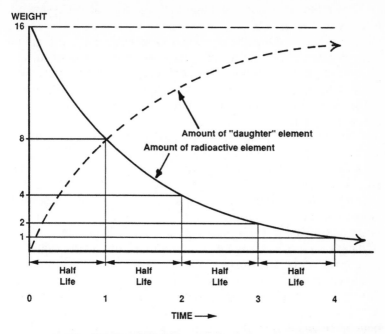

Fig. 26. The half life of radioactive elements.

it first came to the surface. If the process were in practice as simple as this then it would certainly be a means of dating the rocks. There are however many objections, and furthermore there has recently been found a factor that completely cancels the dates of millions of years that the method usually gives.

2. OBJECTIONS TO THE METHOD

The main objections are not directed at the very skilful techniques that are needed for measuring these very small amounts of material, but at the enormous assumptions that are made in interpreting the results. These assumptions have to be made as otherwise the whole basis of the method would be undermined.

One of the best publications that gives up-to-date details of the quite large number of methods of dating both geological and archaeological samples is by Aitken [56], which I will be referring to at times in this section. He does give some of the difficulties and resulting discrepancies that arise with most of the methods, but there is a general assurance that the reader can have confidence in the final established datings — a confidence, as I hope to show, that is unwarranted.

The main objections to radiometric dating of rocks are as follows.

i) It is assumed that there were no daughter products present in the rock when it first came to the surface. As we have mentioned, this is a very large and quite unproveable assumption. If there were only a very minute amount of the daughter element already in the rock, then it would immediately give a date that would make it look as if it was many millions of years old.

The quantities of radioactive material that scientists have to deal with are incredibly minute. Potassium forms only a small portion of rock material. Of the normal potassium, only 0.0118% is the radioactive potassium 40. If argon is present to only 0.05% of the potassium 40, i.e. 0.0006% or 6 parts per million of the normal potassium, then the resulting date is 1 million years [56p121]. It can be seen how easily erroneous dates can arise from minute amounts of daughter elements being present or missed during the technical processing of the samples.

ii) It is assumed that there was no loss of the radioactive element during the decay period. This would again make the rock look older than it was. It is also assumed that there was no loss or gain of the daughter element from the section of the rock that was tested. If the section lost some of the daughter element, then this would make the rock look younger. However, any adjacent area that received some of this daughter element would appear correspondingly older if it were tested.

It is obvious that if these assumptions are incorrect, then the dating of the rock will be quite wrong by very large amounts — and this is precisely what is found. Dates for the same rock, using both different decay elements and even the same element at different places in the strata have been found to give very widely separate ages. A number of examples could be given, but it will be sufficient to quote just a few.

a. Tests on a rock in Nigeria using Potassium-Argon dating 95 million years, using Uranium-Helium gave 750 Myrs, whilst by fission track dating less than 30 Myrs was obtained! [57] The report makes interesting reading, for the authors note that the Potassium-Argon method seemed 'suitable for whole rock dating', but the date of 95 Myrs they obtained was 'geologically unrealistic, for absence of sediment cover, the freshness of the rock and *the ages of associated rocks all point to a late tertiary origin*'.

Here is an indication of how the 'accepted' scale of evolutionary dating overules all discrepant radiometric results, and the puzzlement of the authors in trying to explain how such a wide range of values could arise is very obvious. They conclude that Potassium-

Argon dates 'on other rock basalts must be accepted with caution.' One could suggest that 'rejected' might have been more appropriate.

b. Lava flows in the sea in Hawaii are known to have occurred in the year 1800. When these were dated by the Potassium-Argon method they gave ages ranging from 160 million years to 2,960 million years [58].

c. When Richard Leakey found his famous '1470 Man' that we have discussed in section I H on human 'missing links', the stratum just above it was at first dated by Potassium-Argon at 220 million years [59]. As man is only supposed to have evolved over the last 2-4 million years, this date was quickly dismissed and further tests were carried out using the same basic method on another set of carefully selected samples from the same area. The results varied widely, those from the skull site being 'inconclusive' but other sites ranged from 2.25-4.62 million years [60]. The datings from a site 6 miles (10 kilometers) away of 2.61 million years was considered ' … the best and most acceptable estimate.' and it is this date that has received all the publicity.

This is not the end of the story, however, for three further sets of tests were carried out and even earlier dates were obtained. These ranged from 1.6 to 6.9 MYrs [61], 1.87 to 7.46 Myrs [62] and 1.23 to 2.32 Myrs [63]. Regarding these tests, one sample gave the high values of 7.46-4.11 MYrs. This was blamed upon the presence of 'old detrital K-feldspar' but when the sample was examined for this material none could be found [62]! Indeed, one test on a large crystal (not included in the final table of results) gave a date of 456 MYrs [62]. What is obvious from reading all these reports is how 'anomalous' values are dismissed, and the numerous tests on the acceptable samples allow the workers to claim that this important marker layer is now 'extremely well dated' at 1.88 MYrs [63].

The first dating of 220 MYrs seems to have been ignored simply because it was not in accordance with the evolutionary time scale. It was the second early age of 2.6 MYrs coupled with the size of the skull (probably a small human skull) that made the discovery so famous. The dates were reduced even further by American experts to 1.82 and 1.6 MYrs, as this gave precedence to Johansen's discovery of 'Lucy' as the 'oldest hominid' [24p205]. The latest dating is now given as 1.88 MYrs. The confident stating of this value ignores the wide range of dates that have been dismissed 'en route'.

3. ISOCHRON DATING

This is a very technical method of correlating radiometric isotopes of Strontium and Rubidium material in rocks in order to eliminate some varying factors so that the date will be more reliable. It is difficult to explain the method in a book of this nature, but it is hailed by geologists as a means of providing a firm date for a given rock.

There are two objections however. The first is that the results do NOT give consistent dates for the same stratum. In some tests, the results have no identifiable time significance, and are labelled 'fictitious isochrons' [64]. Specialists in the method have considerable difficulty in trying to 'explain away' anomalous 'pseudo-isochrons' [65] and have to speculate about 'partial melting', 'mixing of crustal components', 'contamination' etc. With such obviously incorrect results, how can the method be hailed as absolute, independent and 'reliable'? A method either consistently provides reliable results or it else it is unreliable. It cannot be both.

The second objection is that these results could be achieved if the materials in the rock came together by a process of mixing, as has been suggested by the experts in discussing the 'pseudo-isochrons'. This is certainly what would have occurred if the different elements were mixed whilst in a solution, as will be proposed and examined in section F4 below on 'A new origin for geological strata?'

4. FISSION TRACK DATING

Instead of normal radiometric decay, a small percentage of Uranium-238 undergoes spontaneous fission decay. If it is embedded in a crystal it creates a minute disruption of the lattice known as a 'track'. The amount of Uranium in the sample can be obtained by bombarding it with a measured amount of neutrons which creates more tracks. By counting the tracks before and after the measured amount of neutron treatment the quantity of uranium can be calculated. From this and the number of fission tracks created by the uranium in the passage of time, the age of the sample can be estimated.

The major difficulty with this method is that the tracks fade over a period of time depending upon the temperature to which they have been subjected, and therefore a correction has to be made for this factor. Furthermore, it has been found that various minerals have different rates of fading.

In order to see the tracks a high-powered microscope (500-2500 magnification) is needed, whilst the time taken to count them is lengthy and tedious. In addition care has to be taken that gas bubbles and other irregularities are not included in the count. There is seemingly rather more dependance upon the dedication and skill of the operative in this method than might apply to other systems.

The KBS tuff referred to the discussion of 1470-man has been given various potassiun-argon ages, and fission track dating was used as a cross check by Gleadow [66]. In this report, two fission track dates of 2.44 and 2.42 Myrs by separate workers was dismissed because 'These ages apparently agree closely with each other but this is mainly due to the close communication between these authors on track identification and discrimination in these samples' [66p225]. From this it appears that concordant results can still be wrong due to collusion between the scientists!

Gleadow claimed that the 'so-called' tuff was actually mixed with older detrital material and deposited as a sediment. To eliminate the older minerals he specifically selected lumps of pumice 'as these represent relatively uncontaminated igneous material'. From these he carefully extracted minute crystals of zircon which gave a fission track date of 1.87 Myrs. Yet in the same lumps were apatite, zircon and sphene that gave two different dates of 25 and 500 Myrs. These were claimed to be older detrital minerals that were *presumed* to have worked their way into cracks in the block of pumice. The blocks were therefore not 'uncontaminated' as he had assumed.

Had the 'appropriate' age of the tuff been very much greater than the 1.87 Myrs finally resulting, there is the suspicion that the 'detrital material' would have been carefully examined, and the young age of the zircon 'explained away'.

As with many papers on dating of strata there is much discussion of discordant results for which speculative reasons are provided. Further criticisms on just this one paper could be made but sufficient has been pointed out to show some of the basic problems and inconsistencies that can arise even though very sophisticated techniques of fission dating are used. Whatever method might be used, the need of all samples to conform to an 'acceptable' date would be a pre-condition.

5. DATING THE GEOLOGICAL COLUMN.

Invariably, when the well known 'geological column' is depicted in books, it has alongside it the ages of the various strata in millions of years. Just how accurate are these dates however and how were they first determined?

A researcher, Adolph Knopf, looked at the first results of radiometric dates that were applied to the column [67]. These first datings are important as it seems that they effectively determined the timescale on the column against which all later dating results had to 'comply' in order to be acceptable.

One would have thought that the first time that the method of radioactivity was used to fix these dates, numerous experiments over a wide range of rocks and ages would have been carefully compiled and analysed before the dates were announced. Such does not seem to have been the case. Knopf gives a revealing account of how unsatisfactory the first three datings were, yet were nevertheless applied to the column. He wrote —

'An urgent task for geology is to determine, in years, the length of the eras, periods and 'ages' (time spans of the stages) and eventually of the zones. Not a single one of them — eras, periods, and ages, let alone zones — has yet been reliably determined. This statement is possibly surprising in view of the fact that almost any modern writer can produce a geologic timetable that gives precise datings and lengths of the eras and systems and even some of the smaller subdivisions ... These figures have been obtained in various remarkable ways. Ultimately, however, they are tied to three dates based on atomic disintegration: 60 million years the age of the pitchblende at Central City, Colorado; 220 million years the age of the pitchblende at St. Joachimstal, Bohemia; and 440 million years, the age of the uranium bearing shale at Gullhogen, Sweden. The age of the Swedish shale is the only one of these that is palaeontologically controlled ... All the other absolute ages have been derived from the three radioactive tie points by interpolation based on thickness of strata or by "reasoned guesses" ... '[67p227]

The dating of pitchblende is unacceptable as a fixing date because when hot it could flow from one level to another before it sets hard. It cannot therefore be used to date any rock in which it may be found. Furthermore, as Knopf says, it does not contain any true fossilised material that could be used to date it by palaeontological methods. This therefore only leaves the Swedish Kolm; but is this any more satisfactory? Knopf comments on the dating of this rock—

'The [dating] of the kolm was determined by Nier, in 1939, and yielded the very disconcerting result that the age, based on Lead 206-Uranium 238, is 380 million years, whereas that based on Lead 207-Lead 206 is 770 million years. Now Nier, it must be recalled, regarded the figure given by the Lead 207-Lead 206 ratio as being the least subject to error and hence the most reliable. For the kolm, however, the figure 770 was clearly too large.' [67p234]

With this large discrepancy, were these results rejected? No, they were simply mathematically combined to give a date of 440 million years, on the *assumption* that some of the Radon gas had escaped and that this had affected the final datings!

Even with these suspect and unsatisfactory dates being used, how were the intermediate ages obtained? As we have seen, by 'thickness of strata and reasoned guesses'. Reasoned guesses can hardly be classed as a scientific method of obtaining dates that span millions of years, and strata thickness is similarly inadequate. It is obvious that sediments in a river can build up very quickly during a flood or very slowly if the material is very dispersed. Knopf quotes one scientist who specialised in sedimentation that estimates of age based on thickness of the strata ' ... are hardly worth the paper they are written on.' [67p228]

We would recommend a reading of this important paper by Knopf, for although he speaks from an evolutionists point of view, he gives considerable information concerning the weaknesses and inadequacies of almost all the radiometric methods used. Often a new process is discovered which raises the hopes of dating rocks accurately, only later to find that it yielded very discrepant results or that there was a basic flaw in either the theory or the technical method.

Although written in 1957, the inadequacy of these first determinations and the widely discrepant dates obtained after many years of experiments that were available even at that time is very apparent. Now that many more dates are reported in the scientific journals, it might be thought that the dates of all the main geological periods seem to be fully confirmed. We have indicated above and will now examine further, however, the way in which numerous discordant results are regularly ignored.

6. 'CONFIRMATION' WITH OTHER METHODS

No doubt many will be surprised by such revelations on the very inadequate way in which the time scale of the geological column was first determined, and the question will be asked 'Surely there are thousands of radiometric datings that have since verified the accuracy of the geological time scale?'

As we have shown even with the few examples given above, there are really enormous discrepancies between dates for one rock, particularly if different methods are used on the same strata. How is it that with such a wide range of results, the final 'approved' datings usually conform to the 'accepted' datings in the geological column?

As far as the high correlation of the published results are concerned, this is easily achieved by running numerous tests on rocks that are found to give the 'acceptable' datings expected. Thus highly consistent results can be published for certain rocks, giving an impression of high accuracy which is spurious. What happens, however, to any 'inconsistent' results?

Most dating results are given with considerable confidence, implied assurance of their accuracy, and often said to correlate with other dating methods. The result is that the public assume that they are precise and reliable dates, but such trust is misplaced. Occasionaly widely different results are sometimes reported in scientific journals and I have examined some of these in another work [24p64-67 and p225-228]. If we take for example the three dates ascribed to Richard Leakey's 1470 Man, these were from 220 M.yrs to 2.6 M.Yrs to 1.88 M.Yrs. With such a range of results, then surely any claim that radiometric dating is an accurate method is unacceptable.

In an earlier work [24p227] I had suggested that before any results were published, they were generally preceded by a series of preliminary or 'pilot' tests that were taken to see if the material was 'suitable' for the particular method used by the aboratory. If they did not give the expected dating the sample would be rejected due to 'contamination', 'migration of the daughter element' or some similar reason for the 'inconclusive' results. At that time I had nothing more to go on but occasional references in these reports of 'unsuitable' results being obtained, but what the dates were was not usually given. It was this that made me suspect that 'trial runs' were being made to check that 'acceptable' dates would be obtained before a full test was carried out and duly reported.

My suspicion that such preliminary tests were undertaken was fully confirmed by a young geophysicist who approached me after a lecture I had given against evolution in January 1991. He had worked in a laboratory that carried out radiometric dating, and mentioned that it was *standard practice* to carry out no less than 12 'pilot tests' on rock samples. The geologist also had to give the 'expected range' of dates, and if the results were outside these 'acceptable' values, the whole sample was rejected and another core from the same rock was used for a second series of pilot tests. By these means we can see how it is that the conforming of all published results to acceptable values is assured.

He also noted that a plot of the results were often an almost random distribution of dots. He challenged a senior scientist about this and said that really you could draw a straight line almost anywhere on the page and call it a 'resulting date', to which he agreed!

Often in articles in which dates have been given, it is claimed that these results 'are confirmed by' some quite different method of dating. This greatly strengthens the claim that the dating of the sample is now firm and irrefutable. But is this so?

As we seen, samples have to be accompanied by an 'expected date', and any results well outside this figure can be rejected. As this will apply to all dating methods, it does not take much perception to see that of the range of dates that could be given to any sample, only those complying with the acceptable dates will finally be reported. With this approach in operation, the necessary confirmation of a date is ensured by other techniques, for they must all fall within an acceptable range.

To those who have always assumed that scientific data is, like Caesar's wife, 'above suspicion', such revelations as these may be disturbing. It must be repeated that these criticisms are not levelled at the physicists who carry out the measurements on incredibly minute amounts of material. What is unacceptable, however, is the assumption made in interpreting those measurements into a time scale of millions of years. The results are presented as though they were accurate and reliable, but they are all based on these large assumptions, many are very discordant and the results must fit the evolutionary time scale or be rejected. It could be said that the main reason for the frequent use of radiometric dating is that it is the only test that invariably gives results in millions of years, which is the scale of time that evolution *must* have in order to operate.

Indeed, it does not take too much research to discover that ever since Charles Lyell paved the way for evolution in 1830 by ascribing vast ages to the geological strata, every method of dating from that time has had to conform with this view or be ridiculed in the scientific press. It is little wonder that evidence supporting a young age for the earth hardly ever appears in scientific journals. Such is the power of the 'consensus of opinion' to force at least an outward compliance on those who fear being classed as heretics.

Even though there may be large discrepancies, it may be thought that nevertheless the radiometric dating methods discussed above and those that follow all indicate an age of the earth that is in millions of years and not the few thousand that young-earth creationists propose. We will in section III F 1 show how all these supposed millions of years can be condensed into a short span of less than 10,000 years.

C. CARBON 14

In the section above we have been considering the radioactive method of dating rocks which gives results usually in millions of years. This should not be confused with dating by the radioactive decay of Carbon 14 (C14 or radiocarbon) which is only for organic remains and gives datings less than 50,000 years. The method used is as follows.

1. THE METHOD

At a high level in the stratosphere, powerful cosmic rays strike the air particles and this produces a form of Carbon that is similar to ordinary Carbon but has an atomic weight of 14 instead of the normal 12. This form is unstable and eventually decays into other products, having a half life of 5,730 years. This radioactive carbon in the air becomes part of the normal food chain and is absorbed into the tissues of plants, humans and other animals. In living tissue, the loss and decay are eventually balanced by the intake of more C14, and a steady condition of a low constant level of C14 content exists. When the animal or plant dies, it absorbs no more C14, and the amount in the tissue slowly decays. By measuring the amount of Carbon 14 that there is left in the organic material under test, it should be possible to work out how long the tissue has been dead. However, there are several important problems inherent in the method.

2. THE CRITICISMS

a) **The high generation rate** — a major factor.

As with radioactive dating, there is the general assumption that the rate of decay that is measured today has been unchanged for many thousands of years. One variation that scientists have tried to allow for is the amount of carbon that has been released into the atmosphere from fires and furnaces since the the beginning of the Industrial Revolution. This has had the effect of diluting the amount of radioactive carbon absorbed by plants, but corrections to the datings can be made. There are much more fundamental variations than this, however, that throw serious doubt upon the dates that the method provides.

To simplify the argument, it will be assumed that the *rate* of decay would not have changed significantly over the last few thousand years which is the time range over which the C14 method is used. What is disputed is that the *amount* of C14 in the biological system in past times was very much less than it is today.

When the scientists first measured the amount of C14 in living material, they found that there was about 1.63 'units' (disintegrations / sq. cm / second) on average and they assumed that this had been constant for a very long period of time. They did notice however that the amount of C14 that was being generated in the upper atmosphere was actually at the much higher rate of 2.5 'units'. This is a difference of some 50% between them, yet it is consistently ignored.

The most obvious explanation for this difference is that the level today happens to be 1.63 (at sea level) but that it is still slowly rising to the value of 2.5 which is the rate of generation in the upper atmosphere. When the amount at sea level reaches 2.5 it will then be stabilised at this figure uniformly. If this factor of present day change is taken into account it makes a very considerable difference to the dates obtained.

Fig. 27 shows the assumptions made in obtaining a date from a C14 test. It is assumed that the object, say a piece of wood, had 1.63 units in it when it died. Over the years, the amount of C14 in it would decrease along the descending curve. When the scientist measures it today and finds that it has only 0.3 units, he can work out from the shape of the curve how long the piece of wood has been dead and he assumes that when it died it had the normal level of 1.63.

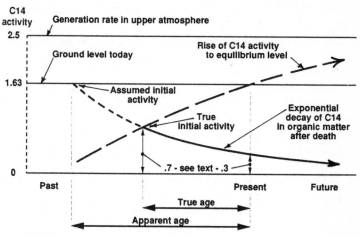

Fig. 27 Carbon 14 decay — the reduction of the datings.

If however it did not have this amount but started with some lower value of say 0.7, then it would appear very much older than it actually was. Consequently, all C14 tests would give too great an age for a specimen, and the older the apparent age then the greater the error. Indeed, the ages can be recalculated on this basis and all would be less than 10,000 years.

Strangely, Aitken does not mention this difference in the amount of C14 in the upper and lower levels of the atmosphere and in fact states that the 'atmospheric concentration variation would be uniform because of rapid mixing' [56p68]. He does, however, agree that there is a considerable delay in reaching a stabilised condition 'on account of "hold-up" in the atmosphere and surface ocean due to delay in mixing into the deep ocean' [56p68]. He notes that a 1000 year periodic change in the production rate would only alter the concentration at sea level by about .07 of the maximum change [56p74]. A response as slow as this is sufficient to account for the gradual rise of the measured quantities at sea level referred to above as it is only a few thousand years since the Flood or Creation when production of C14 was commenced.

b) **The earth's magnetic field.**

There is one other very important factor that would also result in less C14 entering the biological cycle. This is the earth's magnetic field. This field around the earth is of a shape that tends to deflect the incoming cosmic rays away from the atmosphere (Fig. 28). It has been found that the strength of this magnetic force has been declining comparatively rapidly, thought originally to have a 'half life' of 1,400 years, but this has been shortened even further to a value of 1,200 years [68].

As this magnetic field would have been higher in the past (twice as high only 1,200 years ago), fewer cosmic rays would strike the atmosphere and therefore less C14 would have been generated. Thus in the past the C14 in living tissue would have been less. Tests, based upon the assumption that present day levels have been nominally 'constant' with only a slightly higher level in the past, would again give a time since death that would be too great.

Aitken agrees that the alteration would be significant, for an increase of 20% of the magnetic field would decrease the production of C14 by 10% [56p74]. Whilst he mentions this effect, he dismisses any gradual change as only being short term and reversals of the magnetic field (which we consider later) as being local. This is contrary to the views of experts in these fields, and he does not attempt to correct any of the C14 datings for this important factor. The subject is complex particularly in conjunction with the 'delayed effect' factor referred to above, but effectively to ignore such a major influence is to destroy all credibility in this very complex and sophisticated method that in some cases purports to give accurate dates within 20 years.

Whilst discussing the younger dates that these two factors above would give — all less than 10,000 years of age — I would mention the oldest material of 'known date' that was used in the original calibration radiocarbon dating was only 5,000 years old wood that

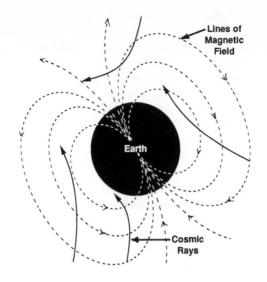

Fig. 28 Cosmic ray deflection by the earth's magnetic field.

was obtained from an Egyptian tomb. Some creationists would criticise the span of dates applied to the Egyptian kings as being too long, and as they form the basis for European chronologies, these too would be incorrect. The works of Velikovsky and Courville both contend that the total period of the Egyptian kings should be shortened by several hundred years. This will be considered more fully in the companion volume.

c) **Calibration of the method.**

In order to obtain consistent results from different laboratories on the same material, they use 'mostly wood dated by dendrochronology' [56p92]. Dendrochronology, or tree ring dating, is a subject we will be examining later. Suffice it to say that this method is even more innacurate than radiocarbon dating, and it is therefore surprising that it should have been used for this purpose [56p66]. The Encyclopaedia Brittanica states that bristlecone pine is of no value for archaeological sites due to its remote and restricted location but that 'Despite this shortcoming, dead bristlecone pine trees are presently providing rings as old as 8,200 years for dating by carbon-14. The purpose is to check the carbon-14 method' [v19p792]. If, as we will see, there is considerable doubt surrounding the dating of the bristlecone pines, this surely places a large question mark over the accuracy of all carbon-14 dates, as the whole system was calibrated by means of an unreliable standard.

We will also see that in some examinations of tree ring datings, radiocarbon dating is used as a guide. The potential problem of circular reasoning in obtaining 'confirming dates' between the two methods is obvious.

The supposed range of 'reliable' dating that can be obtained by C14 is claimed to be up to 50,000 years, the limiting factor being 'contamination acquired during sample preparation' [56p84]. I would suggest that the reliable range may be more in the order of a few thousand years only.

d) **Discordant Dates.**

As C14 dating is only satisfactory for datings of a few thousand years it cannot be used for determining the age of geological strata, but is often used to date sites of human habitation.

Archaeologists have used the C14 method for dating ancient sites but have found that it can give wildly different results. It was reported in an article written in 1975 [59] that one third of these results are rejected by archaeologists and a number of experts have expressed their disenchantment with the method. One might expect that 15 years later the results were now accurate and acceptable. Yet Aitken, writing in 1990, having discussed the numerous 'corrections' that have to be applied to the initial date given by the sample, admits that 'Faced with these aspects it is not surprising that some archaeologists throw up their hands in despair' [56p99].

Possibly to overcome this, when forwarding samples of material for testing, archaeologists are required to give an approximate age they would expect for the sample [56p92]. As with the radiometric dating of rocks, here is surely yet another check to ensure that final published results are not too different from the 'expected' datings.

Aitken, in his book [56], devotes 58 pages to radiocarbon dating alone, a large part of which is an examination of the many (20 or more) factors that have to be considered. The very high sensitivity of the method is indicated by the recommendation that samples should be packed in polythene or glass wool but not PVC, paper or cotton wool as the latter can affect the result [56p89].

With such sophistication and sensitivity, it is little wonder that there is difficulty in obtaining consistent results from the different laboratories and methods used. Indeed, one has the feeling that there are so many 'corrections' that have to be applied that the final results are somewhat contrived. With all these highly skilled techniques being brought to bear, failure to explain the high production rate and to correct for the decrease in the earth's magnetic field, suggests that the scientists have 'strained out a gnat and swallowed a camel'.

As can be seen from the comments above, Carbon 14 dating may be reasonably satisfactory for comparatively recent dates if corrected, but for long ages it is quite unreliable. It cannot therefore be used for dating accurately man's evolution from the apes as this is thought to have taken over 4 million years, or his civilisation occuring in the last 100,000 years.

D. OTHER DATING METHODS

1. TREE RING DATING (DENDROCHRONOLOGY)

This method uses the rings on trees that are produced as the tree grows. Usually one ring grows each year and the rings vary in width and position depending upon the dryness of the season, rate of growth etc. By examining very old trees scientists contend that they can correlate the pattern of the rings in trees found locally with those that have been felled and perhaps used in ancient dwellings. By this means they say that they can correlate datings as far back as 6,000 years.

However, whilst there are bound to be some parts of the ring pattern that are very similar, the actual degree of correlation may not be high. Furthermore, the assumption that only one ring is formed each season is not necessarily correct as more than one can be formed in a year or some rings may be 'missing'.

The correlation of the rings is a fairly subjective matter, for where they (almost) seem to match (but not quite) who is to say that the match is sufficiently near to be acceptable? As many as 30% may be 'extra rings' and 10% can be 'missing' rings [69] which would make correlation impossible. Aitken admits that there are 'missing rings' and 'false rings' [56p38], and that 'because of such irregularities experience and understanding on the part of the operator are essential ... ' [56p39]. This hardly conforms to the requirement of repeatability of experiments by independant laboratories.

Extensive use has been made of the slow growing bristlecone pines. The rings of this tree are very narrow, with as many as 100 in 1 cm, which makes it very difficult to check for correlation between two samples. The tree is also sensitive to climate, which varies the spacing and width of the rings. This makes cross correlation easier, but also means that more than one ring may be produced if there are two wet periods in a year.

To correlate between two trees it may be required to match a pattern in several hundred rings on one tree with several thousand on another. How do the experts begin such a lengthy task? To establish a rough correlation of age between various sections of the two trees to limit the time taken to search the whole section of a tree *they use carbon 14 dating*. As was mentioned when discussing radiocarbon dating, the main calibration curve for this method was based upon the ages of samples established by tree ring dating of bristlecone pine. When this technique is used, there is obviously circular reasoning should it then be claimed that the dates are 'confirmed' by radiocarbon dating methods, or when radiocarbon dates are 'supported' by tree ring datings!

The most surprising aspect of the whole subject of tree ring dating is that the studies of the bristlecone pine was initially the work of only one laboratory. Furthermore, despite several requests to inspect the original material, one researcher was refused access to the data upon which so much has been claimed [69]. Such a practice is hardly conforming to normal scientific standards of behaviour, and if a creationist group were to adopt such an attitude, the reaction of evolutionists is best left to the imagination.

2. VARVES.

As glaciers melt during the summer, they deposit a small amount of the silt they carry into the lake that usually forms at the foot of the glacier. This silt settles out and forms a thin layer on the bottom of the lake. It is assumed that one varve, as each layer is called, is formed each summer and therefore by counting them, a time scale can be obtained. It is claimed that particular patterns of thick and thin varves can be traced between several lakes, and therefore datings going back for some 20,000 years can be correlated. As with tree ring dating, however, it has been shown that more than one varve can be laid down in one season, thus totally undermining the whole method. For example, one expert gave a period of 129 years to a sequence that another expert had said took 2,500 years to form [70]. Despite such discrepancies, it is still occasionally referred to as a valid method.

Sedimentation experiments

Some recent experiments have damaged even further the validity of the varve method of dating sediments. Berthault [71] poured a mixture of sand and powder into a dry funnel and found that it automatically sorted itself into thin layers about 2.5mm thick. He also poured mixtures into a vessel filled with water, and *after* the material was deposited on the bottom, it similarly segregated itself into a series of distinct thin layers also about 2-3mm thick. These experiments show that layers in strata can be deposited very rapidly, and to assume that each one indicates one years deposition is not necessarily correct.

Sedimentation experiments involving water flowing along a channel have also produced some surprising results. As the water flows along the flume, the different sized material it carries settles out as a comparatively thick bed that grows along the flume in the direction of the flow. The material, which starts out as a mixture, falls over the far end of the bed and thereby increases its length, but as it does so, it sorts itself into clearly distinguishable thick *horizontal* layers that can have thinner bands of material within them.

The results of various sedimentary experiments have been summarised [72], a striking result being the flume experiments in which dune-like shapes are formed. Even more unexpected are the layers that can develop cross bedded to others very similar to the nonconforming strata illustrated in Fig. 1.

These surprising results and their similarlty to the complex many layered strata in the geological column is obvious. These experiments however are on a small scale, and it remains to be seen if this mechanism can be applied to explain the present large scale layered sequences that are encountered in the field. Other factors such as flocculation or electrostatic charge may be found to have an important bearing on sedimentation, but if this newly discovered phenomena can be applied, it would involve a major reassessment of geological theory for both creationists and evolutionists.

3. THERMOLUMINESCENCE

It is claimed that thermoluminescence (TL) is suitable for dating pottery and minerals up to about 100 Millions years of age. It depends upon the fact that alpha, beta, gamma and cosmic rays affecting a crystal generate free electrons that move around the crystal lattice. A free electron is eventually captured by an irregularity in the crystal lattice that is deficient of a negative ion, and the electron is 'trapped'. Raising the temperature gradually releases these trapped electrons, the more securely held ones held in 'deep' traps coming out last. Some of these released electrons recombine with luminescence centres and in so doing light is emitted. This light can be measured with a photomultiplier as the sample is heated up to 500°C. This gives a measure of the total amount of radiation received.

Pottery, whether buried in archaeological sites or of antique value is often dated by thermoluminescence. This is because the firing of the pottery when it is made heats up the crystals, releasing all the trapped electrons and thereby setting the 'clock' at zero. As time passes, further free electrons become trapped, and it is these that are measured to give the date since firing.

This of course is a very simplified account of the process of how thermoluminescence operates. Despite all the investigation of the atoms and crystals that there has been, Aitken admits that 'The details of the mechanism by which TL is produced in any given mineral are not well understood' [56p143].

The main radioactive sources of the damaging rays that generate the free electrons are potassium, thorium and uranium. These are not all within the specimen, however, but may be in the earth in which the specimen is buried. Because of this, determining the yearly amount of radiation to which the sample has been subjected over a long period is one of the many difficulties of the method. Very sophisticated techniques have been developed over the years to correct for the many variables that have been discovered as research has progressed. As an indication, Aitken gives a simple three factor formula for determining the age of a specimen, and then comments 'In practice there are many complications and *several dozen measured quantities* go into the calculation' [56p143].

There are many factors that affect the results, such as earlier heating unknown to the testing laboratory, moisture content, grinding of the sample, external beta rays affecting the outer 2mm which has to be removed, and many others. Even pouring of the grains in the preparation can affect the date. This latter is one of four or more effects that give 'spurious TL' that can 'result in an age of several thousand years being obtained for a sample that was only fired recently' [56p147].

It is interesting to compare the approach of the archeaologist (who will trust 'acceptable' dates) with that of the scientist (who is aware of the inaccuracies) regarding the reliability of the method. In the Encyclopedia Americana (1990) the archeaological section outlines the method with little questioning of its reliability [v2 p196]. In a separate volume the scientific description notes 'The physics of the phenomena is poorly understood ... Electron traps seem to be associated with defects and impurities in the (crystal) lattice ... Accuracy is less good than with radiocarbon dating. Geological dating of minerals is more difficult' [v26 p655]. The description in the Encyclopaedia Britannica (1988) is even more damaging for its begins 'Hope rather than accomplishment characterizes the status of thermoluminescence dating' [v19 p790].

Once again the uncertainties of the method can give rise to a considerable range of dates. In another work I have examined the inadequate way in which this method was used deliberately to discredit the archaeological discoveries of Charles Dawson, making them appear to be modern fakes he had fabricated. This allegation was made in order to blacken his character so that his (apparent) responsibility for the Piltdown Fraud would appear to be even more likely [24p38f].

4. ELECTRON SPIN RESONANCE

Electron spin resonance (ESR) is used in much the same way as thermoluminescence, in that it measures the number of trapped negative electrons in the crystal lattice. This is done, not by raising the temperature, but by resonating the electrons. The sample is placed in a strong magnetic field that is varied whilst a high frequency signal is applied at the same time. As the strength of the magnetic field is varied, certain electrons resonate and the absorption of the magnetic field is increased. At particular frequencies, the amount of absorption of the magnetic field gives a measure of the number of the trapped electrons that are resonating.

The difficulties in the preparation of the samples and the tests to measure the annual dosage of the rays are much the same as for thermoluminescence. There are the same problems with unknown heating, grinding the sample, removal of 2mm of the surface etc. There are additional difficulties due to the materials that ESR can date which includes stalactites and stalagmites, shells, teeth and bone. These present their own problems in determining their age because the concentration of the trapped electrons can vary across the section of the biological sample.

As the biogenic material is porous two theoretical models have to be used. The Early Uptake (EU) model assumes that all the radioactive material entered into the sample soon after it was buried. The Linear Uptake (LU) model assumes that it gradually increased over the period of burial. If there are no indications which model may have been operating, then both dates are given. For several samples from one quoted site, the youngest EU date was 240,000 years whilst the oldest LU date was 530,000 years [56p199].

On another site, two final dates were 96,000 years (EU) and 115,000 years (LU). It was decided that the LU date was the more appropriate one as 'Uranium-series dating of the dentine of one of the teeth gave an apparent age of 20,000 years [!], suggesting delay in the arrival of uranium and hence that the LU model was more appropriate' [56p198].

I give these two examples to illustrate the range of dates that may be obtained by ESR can be as wide as those given by most other dating methods that are used.

5. PALEOMAGNETISM

Certain magnetic minerals will align themselves with the earth's magnetic field when their temperature is high, and this is retained as they cool down. This phenomena is used for the dating of both pottery and geological strata.

The position of the magnetic poles changes over the years. When a pottery kiln is fired, the magnetic molecules align themselves with the existing direction and dip of the earth's magnetic field at that time. Knowing the position of the magnetic poles for that period enables scientists to obtain an estimate of the date when the last firing took place.

In geological investigations, it is claimed that by taking samples in different places and depths the position of the North and South magnetic poles could be determined as they varied over the years. It is said that since the Late Tertiary the poles have been in roughly the same position as they are today, but in earlier times there was considerable movement.

A further factor is that the continents are thought to have drifted across the earth's surface (plate tectonics). This would vary the directions of the magnetic strata even if the poles did not move. As the magnetic poles are moving slowly even today, then with the added factor of the continents moving, correlation of all the data would be particularly difficult in trying to go back over a period of millions of years. The folding and buckling of some strata in mountainous areas would give added complications. Local variations that can be quite large add further factors that would have to be allowed for.

Aitken gives an interesting example of interpretation of results. The various lava flows of Mount Etna are 'dated by mention in historical documents' and were therefore thought to be very suitable as data for a reference curve for the method. However, the dates given by the investigation 'led to the conclusion that many of the historical dates may be erroneous' [56p246]. Thus on the basis of archeomagnetism, the history text books would have to be rewritten!

Reversal of field.

A second phenomenon that is really separate from the wandering position of the magnetic poles is the claim that they have actually reversed their polarity numerous times in the past. This is concluded because many rocks have a direction of magnetic field that is opposite to the normal field. This work has been carried out very extensively so that now the whole geological column has been catalogued on a world-wide basis with specific classifications for periods of reversed magnetic field.

Despite all this work, the experts have no satisfactory explanation of how the earth reverses its polarity, and even suggest that some rocks have a natural property of self-reversal of their field. If this is the case, then surely certain rocks under particular circumstances could generate their own magnetic field.

The usual explanation of what creates the magnetic field is that the core of the earth (which is below the crust and the mantle) has a solid centre and a fluid outer section, and that it is the circular rotation of this fluid that generates the earth's magnetic field (the dynamo effect). If this were to be the case, then there is no known mechanism that could possibly reverse such a flow that would generate the reversed polarity that is claimed to be recorded in the rocks. If the flow were to be reversed, the resulting stress upon the mantle and crust above would be sufficient to disrupt them completely. The ensuing massive earthquakes would be world-wide and completely catastrophic.

Furthermore, the drift of the magnetic poles is interpreted as the outer layer of the core rotating more slowly than the mantle and crust [56p230]. If this were so, then the drag of the core on the rotation would have slowed the earth's spin comparatively quickly, making it stationary in a period of time far too short for the evolutionary time scale!

Prof. Barnes has examined this whole subject in depth, and contends that the simplest explanation is that the magetism is due to circulating *electrical currents* in the earth's interior [73]. The reason why this is firmly rejected by evolutionists is that once the current eventually decreases to zero due to resistance, then there is no known mechanism that can provide any further magnetic field. According to the electrical generation theory, the current should be decreasing, and this is precisely what is found.

The failure of the scientists to allow for the considerable influence of the earth's decreasing magnetic field on radiocarbon dating has already been considered. Aitken, however, does acknowledge that there has been a decrease over the last 1000 years (and wide variations earlier than that) on a graph that he gives [56p253].

Barnes, in the course of a paper on the decrease in the earth's magnetic field [73] refers to this subject of the reversed polarity of magnetisation of strata and the following are some of the criticisms that he makes.

i) A precise Silurian sedimentary strata that had been laid down over a short period of time had both normal and reversed polarity at various positions along its length. At another site, normal and reversed polarity in the same strata were found, sometimes in close association, indicating that it could not be due to reversal of the earth's field as all samples would have been affected.

ii) A specialist in the subject suggested four possible mechanisms that could cause reversal, and within two years two of them were verified.

iii) Lightning can magnetise rocks, and it has been suggested that this might be the cause of much of the scatter of the results obtained.

iv) Stress on some materials can cause them to become magnetised (magnetostriction), and this could be a further factor in producing the present magnetic 'anomalies'.

The magnetic field of the earth can vary almost from day to day, for during the 11 year cycle of solar flares that create magnetic storms on the earth, a sever storm can move the effective Magnetic Pole up to 10 degrees from its present position for a short period. Furthermore, some scientists have also claimed that in past times the poles have wandered over most of the face of the earth. With such large and unpredictable variations in both position and strength as we have outlined above, any measurement that uses the earth's magnetism for dating, or in which it has an important effect such as Radiocarbon, is surely quite innaccurate and unreliable.

6. FLUORINE DATING

It has been found that when a bone is immersed in water containing fluorine, the hydroxiapatite slowly changes into fluorapatite. This has been used to obtain a date for the burial of skeletons or other similar organic materials.

The two great problems with the method is that firstly it assumes that the fluorine content of the permeating water has always been the same as the amount measured today, and secondly that the flow of water has been similarly constant.

The first is an obvious problem which cannot be checked, which means that there is no correlation of fluorine content related to a known archaeological date. The second makes the method suitable only for comparing the fluorine content of fossils taken from the same excavation at the same level. If the Fluorine contents of two supposedly closely positioned fossils are different, then there is the possibility that one was placed there at a different time, either by ground movement, an intrusive burial or fraudulently inserted. This is about the only legitimate use for the test. The method is useless for dating fossils from various sites.

Despite such obvious limitations, it was used on the Piltdown fossils [24p8] and the Galley Hill skeleton [24p81f]. Regarding the latter, the skeleton was rejected as being a recent burial as it has a lower fluorine content than the Swanscombe skull. But the skull was in gravel half a mile (1km) away whilst the skeleton was encased in a clay which would have greatly reduced the flow of fluorine to the bones. These factors were dismissed in the report which was clearly intent upon removing this awkwardly early skeleton from the record of man's supposed evolution.

Fluorine profiles.

A recent variation is to plot the depth of penetration of the fluorine into the surface of bones using a nuclear microprobe. Independent of the fluorine concentration, a graph of the fluorine content will be uniformly flat for an very old bone, but will reduce rapidly with depth for a recently buried bone. The method is not accurate however and is used at times as a rough guide of age for selecting which dating technique should be used [56p219].

7. AMINO ACID RACEMIZATION

As discussed above, amino acids are one of the basic building blocks of living organisms. There are two forms — left (L) and right (D) handed — of which only the L form is ever found in organisms. After death, the L form slowly converts to the D form until there is an equal amount of both forms. Measurement of the ratio D/L gives an indication of time since death.

The major difficulty with this method is that it is extremely sensitive to the temperature to which the sample has been subjected over time. An increase of only 1 [°] C increases the racemization rate by about 25%. As the temperature history of the sample can only be assumed, the margin of error inherent in the method can obviously be considerable.

In addition, as water is needed for the racemization, dry conditions also affect the results. The various amino acids vary in their rates and whether they are part of a long or short molecule. With such widely variable factors, little reliance should be placed upon the dates that this method gives. Aitken in fact quotes an interesting case where TWO dating methods were shown to be unreliable.

A Californian skeleton was dated by amino acid racemization as being 40-60,000 years old, the tests being calibrated by using the Laguna Beach skeleton that had been dated by conventional radiocarbon at 17,000 years. When the latter skeleton was later redated using an accelerator-based radiocarbon technique, it gave a date of about 5,000 years, 'thereby reducing the amino acid dates by the same factor' [56p211] — presumably from 50,000 to 15,000 years. This example only confirms just how unreliable are the dates provided by radiocarbon and amino acid techniques.

8. A SUMMARY OF DATING METHODS

There are a number of dating techniques that are said to be suitable only for certain types of samples and limited ranges of ages. These two aspects are summarised in Fig. 29 which is after Aitken. I would emphasise again that this information is provided from an evolutionary point of view, and the accuracy, limits and applicability of the various methods are certainly considerably less than are warranted by the seeming authority of such publications and diagrams. I would also mention again that we will be examining later a subject that effectively reduces all dates that are based on radioactivity to an age of less than 10,000 years.

E. THERMODYNAMICS (The Laws of energy)

There are two fundamental laws of energy that scientists have never yet been able to falsify.

The *first law* states that the total amount of energy in a closed system is constant. 'Closed' means that no energy leaves the system or enters from the outside. The energy within this closed system may change from one form to another but the total amount will be the same. For example, a falling weight has energy, but when its strikes a solid body it stops. Its energy is converted into heat because the atomic structure where the bodies collided becomes very distorted locally and heat is generated. The amount of heat energy is exactly equal to the energy that the moving object had before the impact. The form of the energy has changed but not the total amount.

It will be obvious that the total amount of energy within the universe is constant, subject as it is to this first law.

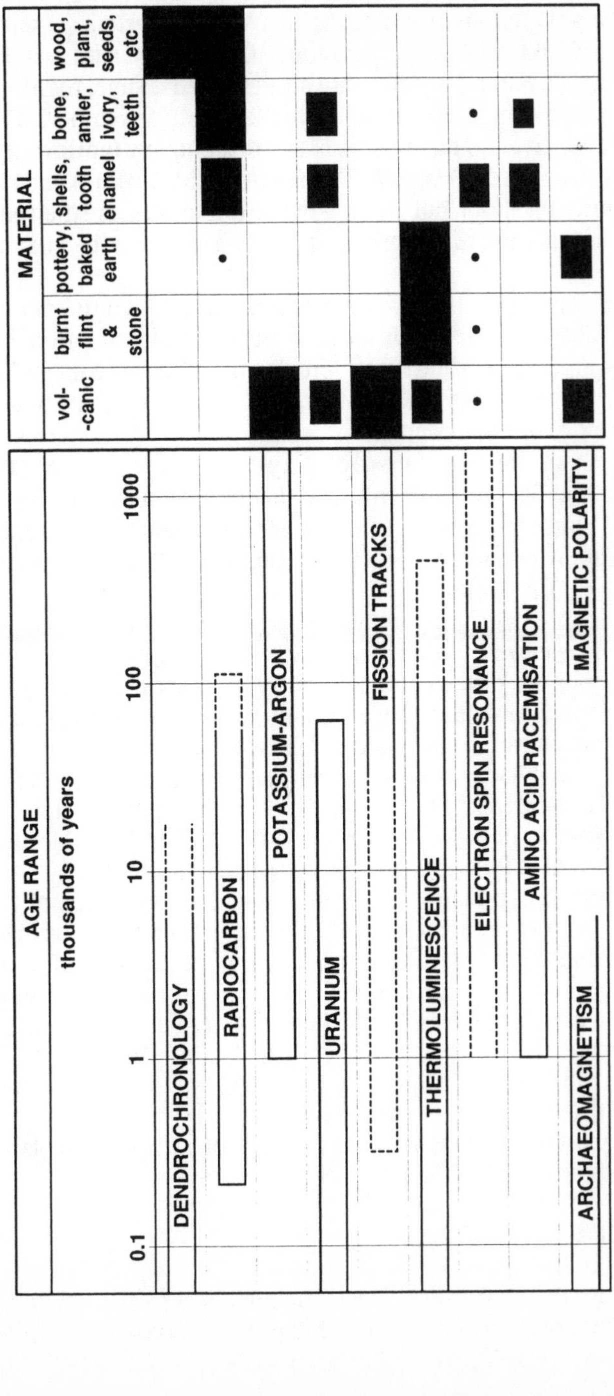

Fig. 29. Dating methods — age ranges and materials (after Aitken)

The *second law* says that the energy within a closed system (such as the universe) is 'running down'. When a system (e.g. the universe) is all at the same temperature, then it can be said that the atoms are all 'uniform', i.e., they are all in the same state, there are no areas where the temperature is higher than any other. The scientific label given to this state is to say that *entropy* (uniformity, randomness or disorder) *is high*. The atoms are all uniform and are randomly moving about, not moving in one direction more than any other, and not moving more rapidly (hotter) in one area than in any other.

[By the way, never be afraid of scientific jargon words such as 'entropy'. They invariably describe a very simple situation for which they are only a 'shorthand' term — in this case 'entropy' is only another name for a particular form of 'uniformity' that applies to energy and order in systems.]

Where there are some areas of a system that are hotter than others then they are less uniform, and randomness and uniformity are lower, (Entropy is lower). Life, and indeed all activity, depends ultimately upon the fact that heat flow from one area to another can be used for useful work.

For example, the energy within the complex chemical bonds of timber can be released by burning to raise the temperature locally. The chemical bonds are broken and the energy is released as heat. This release of heat can be made to raise the temperature of water to become steam. This steam can be contained and released under control to drive a steam engine, which in turn can be used to raise water from a mineshaft. Thus the energy has changed its form through several stages before it performs a function that is useful to man. (Chemical molecular bonds to thermal to kinetic energy when the piston is moved).

It is important to realise however where the real source of the energy comes from. The wood used in the fire is from trees that have grown in the sunlight, and these trees have had the property of using (converting) the energy of the sunlight in the formation of very complex chemicals bonds between the various atoms within energy containing molecules. It is this energy that is released when the chemicals combine with oxygen in the air, the wood burns and this eventually drives the steam engine.

From this, it is obvious that the major source of energy on our planet is that which we receive from the sun.

1. ENTROPY

Our Sun is gradually losing its heat, and other stars will cool down also until the universe is all at one temperature. When this occurs, then nothing further can happen for we live by means of the enormous output of energy from our sun. Energy (as heat) is concentrated in the sun, and we use it as it flows from one area to another i.e. warming the earth and being used by the plants to store energy, which is later used as food or wood for burning. Where the vegetation has been buried and altered, the energy can still be used in the form of coal, oil, petrol or gas as we obtain them from the 'fossil fuels'.

The working of the Second Law can be seen in a small scale on earth. Complex machinery like a car reacts with the elements and gradually (or in some cases all too quickly!) becomes rusty. Similarly, organic material decays and returns to the soil in a simplified form, etc. etc. This general tendency for all material to decay is conforming to the Second Law of Thermodynamics.

No exception has ever been found to these two laws, but strangely, evolution seems to contradict the second law. It is as if the universe is like a clock that has been wound up, and is now running down but the evolutionists claim that their particular clock is 'winding up', ie. life is getting better and more complicated! This is in complete contradicition to the general scheme of things occurring in the universe.

When this is pointed out to evolutionists, they usually reply that the second law only applies to a 'closed' system, i.e. one that has no external input or output of energy. They contend that our earth is not a closed system as we have the input of the energy from the sun, and it is this source of external energy that they say would have enabled the complex chemicals to build up.

The creationist answer to this is that not only do you have to have an energy input to create life, but you must also have the energy organised so that the chemicals obtained are patterned according to a useful design and are not random products. It is this need to conform to a design that is the unbridgeable gulf that evolutionists cannot overcome as we have seen in the section dealing with the supposed chemical evolution of life.

As the energy of the sun is claimed to have been dissipating over an immense period of time, all that would happen within the laws of physics is that the earth would warm up slightly, and when the sun has lost its heat, the earth would then cool down again. In order to convert the energy into a living organism, it must be channeled so that particular chemicals are arranged in a specific order. This requires *information*, which in turn requires the conception of a pattern to which the chemicals should conform. Conception however requires a conceiving mind, which is the very thing that the evolutionist will not allow. He is therefore forced to work only with the help of blind chance. In no way, however, can chance produce the complexity of life we see today.

2. PRIGOGINE'S THEORY

One scientist, Prigogine, has tried to overcome the problem of increasing entropy by claiming that mathematically it is possible for an open system (where energy is flowing in and out) that is 'metastable' (not in equilibrium) to reach a higher state, and this in turn to be driven to a higher state still, until eventually a permanent complex state appears and is stable. His mathematics are extremely complex, but at the root there lies the still unsolved problem that the resulting system must have an ordered structure that is able to keep it in a permanent state.

Prigogine's theory really only applies to physical states, and even then it has been criticised by other scientists. Furthermore, even he has admitted that he cannot see how it could operate in the field of biological species, for he says 'Unfortunately this principle *cannot* explain the formation of biological structures' [in CRSQ v27 p60 September 1990]. In view of this, to press his theories into supporting evolution is totally unjustified.

His work has been hailed as 'legitamising' evolution and theories of changes, and inherent improvement in social systems following in its wake have been suggested. Any such changes would only be a re-enactment of the way that social changes were ruthlessly applied when Darwin's theory was used to justify revolutions and great economic upheavals.

There are evident difficulties in trying to apply his ideas to the real living world and not as simply to a mathematical abstraction. Despite this, evolutionists are so keen are to find a theory, even a poor one, that might suggest that the very great problem of entropy can be overcome, that they have given the theory much publicity and support. As a mark of their gratitude for his efforts in at least trying to overcome the impassable barrier of entropy, the academic establishment has rewarded Prigogine with the highest honour that they can bestow — the accolade of a Nobel prize.

3. CRYSTALS

In their efforts to bend all phenomena to support evolution, some scientists have gone so far as to claim that the formation of crystals from a hot solution is evidence of 'order (the crystals) arising out of disorder (the randomness of the heated solution)', and the various shapes as being indicative of 'variety'. But this is quite unacceptable as evidence for the following reasons.

i) The shape of the crystals is rigidly determined by the properties of the chemicals in the solution. There is no variation at this level.

ii) There is no possibility of there being any 'information' encoded in the crystal as it is of a perfectly regular and uniform matrix of atoms. In a living cell, the arrangement of the molecules (e.g. amino acids on the length of a protein) is specific and their sequence contains instructions vital to the correct functioning of the cell.

iii) Crystals are inert and no activity takes place within them. This is in contrast to the emergence of life from any 'primaeval soup'.

iv) The stability of a crystal comes form its form, whereas the stability of a living organism comes from its process or function.

These reasons should be sufficient to demonstrate the weakness of the case for referring to crystals as defying the law of entropy. This comparison of crystals with forms of life is not often mentioned these days, presumably due to its inherent weakness, but a modern version; not dissimilar, has appeared more recently in which a chemical mixture has been found to have some strange properties.

4. THE OSCILLATING CHEMICAL 'SOUP'

It is possible to mix certain chemicals and obtain some patterns which appear and disappear in a sequence. The main chemical reaction demonstrating this is oxidation of malonic acid by bromate. Four chemicals mixtures are prepared and mixed together in a very precise order, with intervals between certain mixings. Blue spots appear after a time, and rings spread out from them, with the centre of the ring oscillating at different periods for the various centres. The dish can be shaken to make the mixtures uniform again, and then after a time, the blue spots arise and the process repeats itself. This whole process can be repeated about six times before the system no longer works.

This experiment is claimed to demonstrate complexity and order coming from disorder, i.e. a reversal of the law of entropy, and that therefore there is the implication that complex chemicals *could* have come from a 'simple' primaeval mixture of chemicals.

As with the case of the crystals, the experiment has certain features which could not possibly arise in nature in the production of living organisms from chemical mixtures.

i) We need to be clear what is meant by the production of 'order'. If you throw a stone into a pond there is a production of 'ordered' ripples. These however are only the result of the natural *physical* laws that inanimate objects follow in all cases. Simple movements and interactions of this nature can hardly be conceived as able to bring into existence such a complex organ as the human mind.

ii) The whole intricate experiment has to be very carefully set up. If only one part of one of the mixture is incorrect, the experiment fails. It is far from being a random process; a human being had to both devise the experiment and then prepare the chemicals and mix them carefully. Without his presence,there would be no possibility of the experiment occuring in nature, but according to the evolution-ist, there was no controlling mind working over the 'primeval soup'.

iii) This is a very special chemical experiment, and took consid-erable devising. If all of the many basic chemical reactions that occur in the cell are supposed to have arisen naturally, the evolu-tionist should be able to point to thousands of similar reactions that would have assisted in the production of 'life'.

iv) The claimed 'order' is not permanent, for the mixture 'runs down' after a period of time. What the evolutionist badly needs is order and complexity that *increases* as time goes on. This experi-ment fails to do this.

These criticisms should be sufficient to show that this very unusual and highly contrived experiment can tell us nothing about the way in which the very complex chemical reactions that occur in the cell could possibly have arisen by natural processes.

F. RECENT DEVELOPMENTS

Although we could have quoted many cases of large discrepancies in datings of strata, it is sometimes suggested that they nevertheless indicate that the earth is many millions of years old in view of the ages given by radioactive dating methods. There has now been found a factor that effectively 'condenses' these vast periods of time into a much shorter time. This is but one result of investigations by the Australian Barry Setterfield into the speed of light [75].

THE DECREASE IN THE SPEED OF LIGHT.

By examining numerous measurements of the speed of light that have been made since the first one in 1675, he found that there was a distinct decrease. Indeed this decrease had been noted by scientists in the 1930's when it was still occurring. The speed of light is a fundamental factor in physical constants, and if this changes it varies many other constants also. We will in this section look at some the far ranging effects that could occur. (For shortness, the speed of light is denoted by 'c' and sometimes the whole subject of '"c"-decay' is shortened to CDK).

1. RADIOMETRIC DATING

One of the important changes is the rate of radioactive decay. A higher speed of light causes the nucleus of the atoms of a radioactive element to decay more quickly. Thus, when the speed of light was very high, as it would have been at the date of Creation, then the radiocative material would decay very rapidly. This would obviously affect the apparent ages of rocks dated by radioactive elements.

Scientists *assume* that the rate of radioactivity as measured today is unchangeable. Therefore, with the amounts of radioactive material and the daughter elements they find in a rock, they claim that it must therefore be millions of years old. If 'c' was higher in the past, then radioactivity would be higher, and these amounts of daughter elements would have been formed in a very short space of time. Indeed, Setterfield has shown that all the apparent 'millions of years' that the dating method gives can all be accommodated within an age of less than 10,000 years.

Setterfield has also suggested that the apparent increase of age with depth of the strata is due to the material arising from different depths within the earth's interior, which is a subject discussed later.

2. ASTRONOMICAL OBSERVATIONS.

Setterfield has examined the whole subject in detail and has found that it answers many problems that have been puzzling astronomers for many years. One of them is important for 'young earth' creationists for it gives a very simple answer to the question 'If you say that we have only existed for a few thousand years, how is it that we can see light from distant galaxies many millions of light years away?' Quite clearly, if the speed of light was very much higher in the past then it could travel these vast distances in a very short period of time.

Other effects that this phenomenon would have are as follows.

i) It explains why we cannot see beyond a certain distance into the universe (as the light has not reached us yet) and why the night sky is dark (known as Obler's Paradox).

ii) Some interstellar gases have been observed to be travelling faster than the speed of light—which is considered impossible. This is explained by the speed of light being faster in the past, and the light from the movement of the gases at that time is only now reaching us.

iii) The universal 2.8 degrees Kelvin background radiation that has been measured.

iv) The explanation for the red shift of the light from distant galaxies is that the speed of their light slowed down in transit, and not that the galaxies are rushing away from each other. In fact it would appear that when the decrease in the speed of light is allowed for, they may be moving closer together.

3. BIOLOGICAL EFFECTS.

Even more intriguingly, Setterfield, after a mathematical examination, has proposed (in a circulated paper) that as the atomic activity is affected, there are changes in what are known as the transport constants which affect such properties as viscosity, diffusion, osmosis, the speed of ions and electrons and others. This would have enormous effects upon many physical and biological operations and the following are some of the results that might have taken place.

a) Plants.

Photon activity would have been higher, giving increased efficiency in plant growth. The resulting lush vegetation would provide the entombed coal, gas and oil that power our modern economy. In addition, the leaves of plants would not have to be so large to collect the sun's energy, so it is interesting that many plants in the early fossil record have very few leaves or needle-like ones. With a decrease in 'c' the broad-leaved trees would then begin to have an advantage.

b) Insects.

Insects breathe by diffusion along fine tubes in the external skeleton that bring the oxygen to all parts of the body. This diffusion process only operates over short distances which limits the size of insects. With higher 'c', diffusion increases and viscosity decreases so that diffusion can operate over a longer distance, and therefore much larger insects can exist. Fossils of very large insects have in fact been found.

c) Metabolism

Lower viscosities and higher diffusion would make breathing

and blood flow easier, thus increasing oxygen intake and reducing strain on the heart. Similarly digestive activity would be quicker and more efficient. Electron and ion movement would have been faster enabling brain activity and nerve impulses to react more quickly. Thus mental activity and speed of reaction would be enhanced. We have here almost certainly a major factor in the longevity of the Biblical Patriarchs.

As can be seen, the ramifications of these changes of physical phenomena are profound, and for this reason Setterfield's proposals should be carefully checked and investigated thoroughly by competent experts. If they are found to be in accordance with the Laws of Physics, then it is obvious that they are a key that is able to explain many features of the fossil record and the Biblical account.

....

The whole subject of the very wide ranging effects that the decrease in the speed of light has had upon the universe is still being developed, but suffice it to say that the results are solving many problems that creationist have been examining for many years. The whole proposal has been subjected to much unjustified criticism from the secular world and unfortunately from within the creationist movement also. However, Setterfield almost invariably has been able to demonstrate where the criticisms are in error. Much further work has to be carried out, and it is hoped that the latest results will be included in the companion volume to this work on Genesis.

4. A NEW ORIGIN FOR GEOLOGICAL STRATA ?

In addition to the effect that the speed of light has upon radioactive dating results, Setterfield has proposed a model of how geological strata could have been laid down by the action of water deep in the earth's interior. This is known as supercritical or hydrothermal water and would be under extremely high pressure and temperature, being heated by the higher radioactivity in the centre of the early earth. Supercritical water has the property of dissolving large quantities of material which it will carry with it to the cooler surface of the earth. As it rises and cools, different critical low temperatures will be reached for the various materials, and they will be rapidly deposited at different stages. Geologists are now beginning to recognise the importance that this mechanism has in forming much of the geological strata.

Stanton, a senior geologist, has suggested [76] that many rock and clay strata are the results of *chemical* precipitates rather than the slow erosion of previous strata over millions of years, or the molten intrusions from great depths. Although he was only dealing with precipitation over small areas, this principle could be applied over much larger areas.

Stanton proposed that clay could be produced when the hot slightly acid spring water containing much dissolved material flows or pulsates over the sea floor which is cold and slightly alkaline. As these chemicals reacted they would generate a vast volume of precipitates that would very rapidly choke and engulf all sea creatures. This would produce the fossils of fish eating smaller fish and others giving birth to their young that have been found in the strata indicating that they were buried very rapidly.

As the dissolved materials were forced to the surface, they would become very mixed. This mixing process would explain the seeming consistency of isochron dating described above, a method whose reliability is more apparent than real.

Furthermore, most geologists assume that the igneous strata reached the surface of the earth as a molten mass that would take a very long time to cool [77p185]. But if the materials reached the cooler surface as a saturated solution of the many chemicals from the hot interior, they would condense out as a crystalline deposit at a fairly low temperature, and a long period of cooling would not be necessary.

The rising material would bring radioactive elements with it, in quantities that would depend upon the depths from which they are arising. If the centre of the earth has more of the heavy radioactive elements, then material from the shallower layers would have progressively less. The dissolved chemicals from the shallower layers would reach the surface first, to be overlain by further layers from progressively deeper sources. Thus the finished deposited strata would have a very rough grading of rocks with rich radio-active content over those less rich in a progressive series. This could be the explanation for the apparent increase in age with depth of strata, as we have already mentioned when discussing radiometric dating.

One result of this chemical origin of minerals is that it can explain the existence of very large volumes of pure material, particularly clays, that are very uniform in texture and colour (sometimes a light colour) and unmixed with other material. When a range of strata is eroded and re-deposited by being washed off the mainland, as they are today, the result is a dark grey or brown deposit as witnessed by the colour of the mudflats at the estuaries of rivers.

A similar colour can be achieved by mixing together a small quantity of each of the paints in a painting set which will result in a dark brown colour and not a light colour. I would therefore contend that the vast deposits of a light coloured pure clay could not have been the results of general erosion of a land mass over a long period of time.

Strangly, I have never seen any explanation, by either evolutionists or creationists, of the lightness and uniformity of clay beds that exist. The proposed chemical origin of many of the strata is probably the only process that could explain the purity of the coloration and texture as well as the enormous volume that can be seen in many strata today.

In the Uniformitarian scenario, sand is supposed to be the result of minerals such as granite being broken down and reworked during deposition to produce great depths of sandstone. That sandstone is not derived from weathered granite but from sources within the earth has been proposed [78] in view of the absence of certain minerals in the sandstone that exist in the granite. This gives added support to the thesis that much of the earth's strata may be due to hydrothermal activity.

It is commonly accepted that the large accumulations of oil and gas in the earth's interior are a product of the masses of vegetation trapped there that have decomposed over many years. However, one scientist, Gold, has for some time been claiming that much gas (and oil) is actually chemically generated [79A,B]. There have been some borehole investigations that have appeared to support this very controversial view [80] and this proposal is being seriously considered by the specialists [81A]. Gold has also suggested that deep bacterial activity may be responsible for the production of some strange 'gunge' that has been brought up from great depths [81B].

Gold's ideas have now been fully confirmed in a report appearing in the Daily Telegraph (9th October 1991 p. 1). Oil was found at a depth of 2,800 m (9,000 ft) formed by chemical reactions. Any bacteria is due to contamination.

There is also the amazing yet little known fact that there are vast deposits of hydrated methane frozen in the Alaskan oilfields and under great compression lying in huge quantities on the surface of the bottom of deep trenches in the oceans [82]. These deposits are so large that there is more than sufficient to last not just for a few years but for an estimated 65,000 years. This all adds to the claim that such quantities could not have come from the decay of vegetation but from chemical (and/or bacterial) activity deep within the earth's surface, all of which supports Setterfield's initial contention.

These vast deposits of methane would appear to be well within reach of present day equipment but it is claimed that there are problems in developing them. No doubt the financial and political climates will change to allow this abundant and 'clean' fuel to be exploited.

Setterfield has proposed a geological mechanism by which the various strata might have been laid down over a very short period of time rather than the millions of years demanded by evolution. It is surely worth a careful examination by geologists — both evolutionist and creationist — to see if it is in full accord with field investigations.

....

With regard to section F as a whole, although some supporting evidence has been provided, I am conscious that much that has been set out may appear very speculative, It has nevertheless been included in the hope that further research by those who are specialists in these various subjects may be able to prove or disprove each of the proposals. Only in this way can errors be discarded so that we may 'hold fast to that which is good' [I Thess 5v21].

SECTION IV — THE RISE OF EVOLUTION

A. THE PROPAGATION OF EVOLUTION

With all the evidence that has been presented within this volume, those who are convinced by it and agree that the theory is adequately disproven, may well wonder why it is still widely accepted and is so frequently referred to (or is implied) in television programmes and the mass media. The answer is that these important channels of communication are completely controlled by ardent evolutionists who simply will not allow a public challenge to the theory. I have dealt with this subject in more detail elswhere [26p127f] but will give just two general examples of how the public is subtly indoctrinated with the theory, and how writers overcome the many weaknesses the theory contains.

1. TELEVISION PROGRAMMES

One of the most popular types of programme that appeal to all classes and ages are the superbly produced nature documentaries such as 'Life on Earth', 'The Living Planet', 'Survival' and many others. These programmes are costly to produce for they range across the whole globe, penetrating very remote corners, and capture close-ups of rare birds and animals that must have taken many hours of patience and toil. The results are then presented with a polished ease that gives no inkling of the enormous amount of work involved.

What is noticeable however is the evolutionary overtones that such programmes frequently include in their presentation. Such phrases as ' ... millions of years ... ', ' ... survived ... ', and simply ' ... evolved into ... ' occur at intervals. The most often used phrase is ' ... has become well *adapted* to its environment ... ' for which one should mentally substitute ' ... well *designed* ... '. Comments such as these clearly display the evolutionary basis on which the programme has been made. Indeed, it is almost as if these documentaries were a very polished and subtle 'soft sell' for the theory of evolution, so frequently do these phrases occur.

However, at times, the actual behaviour being portrayed is

amazingly complex and unique: many examples could be given.
Rather than list a number, we would hope that the next time a
programme describes some of the marvels of nature on the television, the reader might ask himself the simple question 'How could
that creature (or behaviour) have possibly evolved slowly over
millions of years?' Those that do so should consider the logical
conclusion that if it were not evolved, then it must have been created.

2. THE EVOLUTIONIST'S STRATAGEMS

As the weight of scientific evidence is so much against the theory,
there are some major problems that have to be overcome (or
bypassed) by those who aspire to write books on evolution. After
one has read a number of such books, it become increasingly easy
to spot the particular methods that are used in one form or another
in order to overcome the inconsistencies, glaring contradictions and
inadequacy of evidence that lie at the base of the whole theory. The
same phraseology, arguing of their case, dealing with weaknesses in
the evidence etc. arise so frequently that a distict pattern emerges.
So clear does this become that I have set out in Appendix 4 as full
a list of such stratagems that I could discover.

It will be found that by far the most frequent method used in
books by evolutionists is the way in which the evidence presented
is so very carefully filtered, and contrary information supressed, as
described in section 5 in Appendix 4. If no other information is
given, the reader is left with little alternative but to accept the
conclusions provided by the writer, for he is unlikely to read the
evidence against the theory in the same book.

Is there anything that the reader can do about this?

The most revealing method is to check fully the facts that the
writer may only refer to in a general way. This is difficult, for few
have sufficient background knowledge to be able to refute the
claims that are made by evolutionists.

3.CHECKING THE FACTS

Generally, when anyone reads a book on any controversial issue of
which they have no previous knowledge, it seems very convincing
at first. The author has presented a wide range of facts, deals with
criticisms and then invites the reader to draw the same obvious
conclusions that he has. If this is the only book that is read on the
subject, or he reads other books with the same viewpoint, the reader
will probably be fully convinced by the case presented, and will

lodge the idea with other concepts within his mind. Any such ideas that he accepts may be very significant in the way that he views the world around him.

Where the subject is important (as I believe evolution is), it can have a profound effect upon one's world view and probably one's behaviour also. However, leaving the subject at this stage is dangerous, for one may have unwittingly adopted a false set of values from reading a biased publication. It is therefore essential in such cases that any alternative or contradictory viewpoint should be examined also, in order to determine where the truth really lies.

With so many books, on a wide range of subjects, it is not what *is* stated that can be crucial, *it is what is not stated that is often more important*. This vital evidence however cannot be obtained from a book propagating a viewpoint. Even if the author refers to the contradictory evidence, it is almost certain that it will be misrepresented and significant features ignored, thus enabling him to feel that he has dealt adequately with his opponent's criticism and been able to dismiss it. Writers can always deal with 'straw men' of their own making.

If the reader is unconvinced, and wants to examine the subject further, the first recommendation is to obtain a copy of original papers that may be in the reference section. Often it is unnecessary to go further, as the glaring contradictions, glossed over by the writer of the book, become all too apparent. In many cases, where it is relevant to the theory of evolution, the author of the original paper has to make a reference to the way his results have a bearing on the theory, usually in the summary. This is particularly important where his results contradict the theory, and some such obeisance has to be made at the high alter of evolution if he wants his paper to have any chance of being published.

Unless the reader is prepared to delve into the whole subject in some depth in order to establish the real truth, which is somewhat unlikely in view of the considerable time and effort involved, by far the best course is to read the books by, or speak to, an expert on the other side. It is important that it should be one who is well able to argue his point of view. I have known more than one case where the person chosen to oppose (usually a speaker in a debate) has been carefully selected by the proposer in the knowledge that they are not good at presentation, allowing the proposer to achieve a seeming victory in the ensuing confrontation.

The critic (whether read or consulted) should preferably be an expert or have some detailed knowledge in the particular field under consideration, for then he will be able to quote the latest research and published papers. He will also be far more familiar with the weaknesses of the case that the evolutionist is presenting. There are numerous books and leaflets that have been produced by creationist organisations for many years, and an enquiry should produce the contrary evidence.

Having obtained this, it can then be presented to the first writer (if he can be contacted) for his comments on these criticisms. This process of seeing the two views argued out in detail I feel is one of the quickest and surest methods of determining where the truth really lies, for the weaknesses of one case will be rapidly exposed by the opponent.

On this subject of ascertaining the truth, I would generally suggest that where a debate on any subject is proposed, it is first divided into specific topics. Each speaker is given a short time to present his views and answer his opponents points on each topic before the next item is passed to. In this way each speaker is forced to answer the pointed criticisms made by his opponent, rather than avoid them in a long speech in which he only presents the evidence that supports his case. I have found this one of the quickest ways of exposing the flaws in any arguments, and at the same time it provides a much more lively meeting.

It was in fact this very method of presenting opposing views that first interested me in the whole subject of creation, and I will digress briefly to relate how I came to be convinced by the creationist's case. This occurred long before I had any interest in Christianity, and it is directly relevant to this subject of becoming convinced by scientific evidence.

I had no interest or knowledge of evolution as a teenager, but in the course of reading I came across the book 'Is Evolution Proved' [49]. This was an exchange of letters between an evolutionist (Shelton) and a creationist (Dewar), both very able and articulate exponents of their respective viewpoints. This method of an exchange of letters was an excellent way in which the opposition could be questioned in some depth on a particular subject and the weaknesses of either side exposed before moving on to the next subject.

It was hearing the best of the evidence from both sides that was the deciding factor that convinced me that evolution had virtually no scientific support of any worth, and that the creationist case was far more in accord with the scientific facts. (Having finished the book, I forgot the whole subject for 20 years, when the matter was raised when teaching in a Sunday School of a liberal church I was attending. My reading of 20 years before was called to mind, but what followed is yet another story!)

However the information is obtained, whether by reading, discussion or debate, it is to be hoped that many will come to the conclusion that the weight of sound scientific evidence is greatly against the theory of evolution. In all my studying of the evidence both for and against the theory since 1968, not once have I found a single 'incontrovertible' fact that supported evolution that could not be completely demolished by evidence and arguments presented by creationists.

4. EVOLUTIONIST'S CATCH PHRASES

We are probably all too familiar with the many phrases used in conversation that are rooted in the concepts of evolution — indeed they were coined specifically to put over the principles and outworkings of the theory in the harshness of everyday living. Such phrases as 'survival of the fittest' are used with no possibility of it being wrong ever entering the mind. In this section we will examine some of the most frequently used phrases and see if they are actually as universally applicable as most people imagine. I have particularly chosen phrases that are commonly used in business, and the reason for this will be made clear later. Examples from the world of commerce will also be given to show that these phrases, convincing though they may sound, do not accurately reflect what actually happens in life.

Survival of the fittest

i) Circular argument

This well-known phrase (along with 'the struggle for existence') has been bandied around for so long that we all tend to accept it and not think about either its logic or its repercussions. But what precisely does this phrase mean?

Let us imagine that one animal, say a horse, is physically able to run slightly faster than most other members of his species because he has longer legs. This would enable him to outrun more of his pursuing predators, and he should accordingly have a better chance to survive and thereby have more offspring who are likely to inherit this feature that gives greater speed. This sounds simple, but, as ever, the real truth is far more complex.

There is a limit to the length of horses' legs. We have already mentioned that continual inbreeding can result in other parts of the anatomy becoming weaker. Similarly overdevelopment of one part of the body must result in more energy being used for this, to the detriment of other parts. Other factors affecting the whole subject could be a decrease in the ability to turn quickly whilst at speed to deter a pursuer, or the greater difficulty in stopping when meeting an obstruction etc., etc. Thus in trying to determine an animals 'fitness', the whole animal must be considered at the same time and not one part isolated for continual improvement.

Biologists would like to calculate the optimum length of legs that a horse should have but so many factors are involved that the task is far too complicated for solution. Neither have they been able to give any form of grading of fitness of the various characteristics that an animal may possess. They therefore had to recourse to the general observation that the only real test of fitness is that those animals that are the fittest will be those that survive in the competition of life and thereby have more offspring. But this is precisely what was being claimed in the first place, i.e., the fittest (now defined as those that survive) are the ones that survive! Thus, this statment is what is known as a tautology — a statement of the obvious. (A simple example of tautology would be the observation; 'The reason why that man cannot see is that he is blind')

If the statement is rephrased, it would be 'A species survives because it is the fittest, and it is the fittest because it survives.' — which is a circular argument. That this is the case has been acknowledged by some writers, but it is little realised by most people. It is still accepted as a true statement, but the the inability of the biologist to define 'fitness' is rarely appreciated.

ii) Elimination of the unfit.

Innumerable television nature programmes (in what amounts to virtual propaganda on the subject) take every opportunity to demonstrate that unfit members of any group of animals usually die early. Nestlings may have one or more weaker members, who are less able to reach the parents to demand their fair share of the food. As a result they become weaker still and eventually die.

There are cases where animals have fed and protected their older or wounded members and they have managed to survive quite satisfactorily, but broadly speaking early death of the weakest does seem to be a general rule. In view of this, rather than there being a law of the 'survival of the (few) fittest', it is probably more accurate to say that there is in nature the 'elimination of the (few) unfit', which puts the whole subject in a totally different light. So long as the animal is reasonably strong it has much the same chance of survival as one that may be stronger. Many animals die in later life due to causes, such as mass starvation or disease, that are mainly independent of their degree of fitness. The fit and the slightly less fit might both perish for reasons that have little to do with their general health, as we will be examining later.

In business, the same applies. Take for example an efficiently run firm, managed by very able directors, staff, salesmen and technicians, and manufacturing a product in demand. It then has a disasterous fire, or, if in the food industry, glass is put in the product by a blackmailer. The result could well be the collapse of the firm. There would then be a wholesale sacking of the complete staff, *for reasons that have nothig to do with whether they are efficient (fit) or not.*

Equally, many companies survive and make a profit even though they may not be the most efficient in their trade. I am sure that many readers will be able to confirm that quite inefficient organisations can still pay their way. Their prosperity may be the result of many factors, such as a high demand for their product, little opposition, specialised services, protected market, etc.

It is therefore suggested that the phrase 'survival of the fittest' does not apply in the way that most people imagine in either nature or in commerce.

Nature 'Red in Tooth and Claw'.

The picture so frequently presented, by television programmes in particular, is that all animals in nature are engaged in a constant battle to either capture prey or escape predators. Films of hunting packs of lionesses and hyenas certainly make fascinating viewing. The idea that then arises is that the predators are necessary to keep the numbers of animals in check. If they did not do so, some herds would expand and overrun a particular area, and the balance of nature would be 'upset'. The hunters are therefore considered to be a vital means of maintaining this balance.

But is this what is really found in nature?

Take, for example, the hunting of the lionesses. They kill only every two or three days, and even then, not every foray is successful; it may take several attempts before an animal is caught. This one meal is then sufficient to last the whole pride of lions until the next kill. Between these times, the pride sleeps and lounges in the shade apparently very relaxed, whilst the cubs play and have their mock fights. They are far from having to hunt continuously to survive.

As far as the number of wildebeestes and other animals they kill is concerned, one animal for each pride of lions every few days would have little impact upon the numbers of the many thousands that roam the African plain, for they only catch 2-3% of the herd

[83p119]. Indeed, one expert has suggested that the lions provide a service to the hunted in that when they are being chased the whole herd charges around very agitatedly at high speed, which is the only real exercise they have from the normal plodding gait they usually adopt!

Experts have examined in considerable detail the habits and inter-relationships of numerous species and some surprising conclusions have resulted.

There is one 'statistic' about predation that appears in many textbooks, which deals with the periodic increase and decrease of both hunters and hunted. A graph of the number of snowshoe hares caught by trappers showed a regular rise and fall over several seasons with a periodicity of 9-10 years. On the same chart was plotted the number of Canada lynx also trapped, and this rose and fell in the same way but always slightly lagging on the curves for the hares. There appeared to be a link between the populations of the two species, and the obvious conclusion was drawn that as the numbers of the hares increased, this allowed the lynx population also to rise a little later as food became more readily available. As the hare population declined, due now to the larger number of lynx, the lynx had fewer catches and their numbers decreased as their food became scarce [84].

This close link between the numbers of the hunters and the hunted was presented as evidence of how the 'balance of nature' was obtained. The numbers of both species were kept in check by the lynx killing the hares, the reducing numbers then limiting the number of lynx that could survive.

This regular rise and fall of predators and prey has been the subject of much theoretical mathematics, with formulae being provided that result in the same variation of the interaction between the two groups. The hare-lynx results have been widely referred to in textbooks and evolutionary biassed publicity, and with the theoretical support it would appear to be well proven. Such is not the case however.

Krebs refers to this example and notes

'The hare-lynx cycle has been interpreted as an example of an intrinsic predator-prey oscillation, but this apparently is not correct. Keith (1983) [86] has shown that food shortages during the winter initiates the decline in hare numbers, and predators play a secondary role in prolonging the decline to low numbers. Although lynx depend upon snowshoe hares, the hares fluctuate in numbers because of interactions with their food plants. No one has yet found a classic predator-prey oscillation in field populations' [85p295]

Once again, a false correlation is used to persuade a gullible public that the struggle for life is a biological necessity.

To give a parallel in the business world, not every company is engaged in one unending battle against competitors in securing a large order using every trick and technique taught by the latest slick salesman's course. There is time for much camaraderie, humour, parties and (for many I would hope) the satisfaction of being engaged in a rewarding and useful occupation. There are also the personal human inter-relationships of the family, friends, hobbies and sports that most enjoy, quite separate from their working life.

Those who are devoted to attaining 'success' in their work at the expense of their family life often find too late that they have paid an unacceptably high price when their children are estranged from them or they are involved in divorce or separation. They may continue with their act of bonhomie, but they are often very lonely people, for they have no sense of the close companionship that is really only achievable within a warm family group.

Such aspects however are totally ignored by the vivid images that are brought into the mind by such trigger phrases as 'nature red in tooth and claw', and the implication that this is an inevitable 'Law' that all must need follow.

'Dog eat Dog'

This is a phrase frequently used in business to emphasise just how remorseless the competition is. If you do not eliminate the opposition first, then they will do the same to you.

But let us ask the question 'Have you ever seen one dog eat another?' Of course not. Neither do eagles kill eagles, or wolves hunt wolves. Therefore the phrase is contradicted by what actually takes place in nature. There are occasions when adult lions kill the offspring of another lion when they become the new head of a group of lionesses. Birds also kill other birds etc. but adults rarely kill another adult of their own species.

When animals do fight one another it is usually over territorial rights or for leadership of the herd of females. In most cases of defending territory, the victor is usually the defender, the invader being chased away. In fights for leadership, the loser may be wounded, but knows when he is beaten and slinks away from the combat. Rarely is one of the contestants killed.

Man, however, is the only species where one adult will kill another member of its own species. Furthermore this is not usually for food or territory, but for more personal reasons. With his incredible ability to reason and plan, man has used this for his own personal advancement or self satisfaction, often against other people to their detriment — even to their death.

Many will claim that they have never killed in their lives, and reject the suggestion that such a charge could apply to them. Yet they will scheme and spread false witness against another whose downfall they wish to see so that they may replace them, or for some other reason. Whilst they may not have committed a crime that could be judged in a court of law, they have nevertheless committed what could be described as 'commercial murder' of another person's reputation. Indeed, we have only to *think* of some such venture, and we will be held guilty [Matt 5v28].

....

The interlinking network of relationships.

It is well recognised how closely interlinked are the lives of animals in their varying environments, and how far reaching changes in one area affect other links also. For example, in China there was a campaign to eliminate the flocks of sparrows that were consuming so much food. The result was a plague of flies and other insects that the birds had kept in check.

One interesting book on this whole subject is 'The Ecological Web' by Andrewartha and Birch [83]. It is carefully researched, wide ranging in its scope, and many of the popular concepts such as we have been dealing with in this section are shown to be without foundation, despite having been promoted by experts. The following is a summary of some of the more interesting findings.

i) One island in Canada was colonised by moose in the early 1900's and the number grew rapidly for a few years when they declined sharply due to overgrazing [83p82f]. Numbers then began to recover. Wolves reached the island in 1948 and they also grew in numbers, but this seems to have had little effect upon the general level of moose population which apparently stabilised around a reasonable figure. The main find was that wolves generally took the young and the old infirm moose amounting to about 63%. The major factor was that malnutrition weakened the moose such that they were less able to defend themselves, the wolves only killing those who were either too young to run away, particularly in deep snow, or the old and feeble. Most mature moose were able to defend themselves adequately. The size of a pack of wolves bore no relationship to the 'kill rate' which was 1 moose every 2.5 days.

ii) In America and Canada many attempts had been made to deal biologically with pests. 674 predators were introduced to control 154 pests, but only 21% of the pests were effectively controlled. This again shows that predation is not an important factor [83p114].

iii) In Minnesota there was a 2 kilometre 'buffer' zone between packs of wolves that was rarely crossed by the members. Deer that happened to winter in these zones were far less subject to predation by wolves [83p118].

iv) Many wildebeests killed by lions were in poor condition and would have died soon if they not been caught. Hyenas also killed about 2% of the herd, many of their victims also being debilitated [83p119].

[Having said this, an article by Smith [87] gives a different viewpoint regarding the state of animals caught by predators. From his enquiries of trappers and rangers he concluded that predators much preferred to catch healthy animals, and that they often ignored weaker members. These were likely to be weakened not just by malnutrition but by disease to which they were more susceptible than a healthy animal. Avoiding them was therefore a benefit to the predator. He does accept that chance is a major factor that decides which animal a predator will go for. He also agrees with Krebs that cycles of population growth and decline have little connection with predation, and quotes papers that refute 'classic cases' supposed to prove this connection.]

v) Darwin's statement that similar species will come into conflict more frequently than animals of a different type is shown to be unfounded. Similar species can occupy the same area and have much the same feeding habits, yet can still exist together without competition [83p141].

vi) Immigration from an area due to dense 'population pressure' is not supported by field experiments. Overcrowding does not seem to be the real cause of individual or mass migrations [83p178].

vii) Local populations of animals may become extinct due to local environmental factors, but the total population of the species is likely to survive because the wide range of the habitats makes it improbable that they will all suffer major environmental changes at the same time. This is called 'spreading the risk' and is an important factor in the survival of species [83p184].

Many similar surprising results are presented in this revealing book which is well worth studying further by those interested in the inter-relationships between animals. Broadly speaking, the main restriction on population is the availablity of adequate and nourishing food, which is itself dependant upon the prevailing weather conditions. On the other hand predation is shown to play very little part in limiting the numbers of a species. From this it follows that the broad assumptions behind the evolutionary catch-phrases we have been examining are completely contradicted by the field evidence.

The social repercussions.

As we have said before, there is far more to life than achieving predominance over others, but these sayings we have been examining are used so frequently and so glibly, that they have entered the folk-lore of the commercial world, and that of the stock phrases of salesmen in particular.

In considering these well known sayings, it should by now be clear that they are not useful shorthand phrases that express a complex idea in a succinct way, but that they are catch-phrases, used to produce a view of nature that is not actually true in real life. These three are just a selection of the many misleading slogans created by the exponents of evolution to persuade an unthinking public that it is no longer a theory. It is considered to be an inevitable 'Law' that applies in all of life, and that as we are little more than an advanced form of animal life, then it is perfectly natural to behave in such a brutal way to others.

What is of further interest is the way in which these emotive phrases have been used less frequently in recent years. The more acceptable phrase of 'adaptation' to the environment is the line now more often taken. 'Survival of the fittest' expressed a world-view that was very much more acceptable to the commercial ethos existing at the height of the Industrial Revolution, when success in competition went to the more unscrupulous of the warring parties. It was therefore frequently referred to by writers at that time, as I have considered elsewhere [24p168f]. These catch-phrases, seemingly with the support of the 'science' of evolution behind them, were paraded as giving sufficient reason for the herding of mass labour into the 'dark satanic mills' of industry. If thousands died prematurely from the terrible conditions they suffered, this was to be expected in a world where only the fittest could survive.

Today, with the appalling social results of such a philosophy being all too apparent, the public are being gently swung to accept the opposite set of values as being the true teaching of evolution. We now have paraded before us the lessons that can be learned from evolution, benefits of cooperation for the common good, and other laudable social activities. We are informed that it was through such relationships that the 'higher species' such as apes and mankind were able to progress to the positions they now have at the pinnacle of the evolutionary tree.

Praiseworthy as such efforts may be, it should not be forgotten that that they are still rooted in evolutionary concepts, and that subtle propaganda is still propaganda all the same. We are all subjected to exceptionally sophisticated forms of persuasion, the vast majority of which we are completely unaware, and its detection requires careful examination and eternal vigilance. Failure to do so will inevitably result in the triumph of those who, for whatever reason, would draw us away from seeking the path of Real Truth. Those who would deny that such influences exist may consider that they are right, but if they are not, then they themselves are the naive targets of subtle and widespread manipulation.

Whilst these moves to revise social attitudes are an improvement upon the older catch-phrases they nevertheless still fail to address much deeper questions such as why this wonderful universe was created in the first place, and what the real purpose is for man's existence. Such thought-provoking considerations are abhorrent to most evolutionists, and are therefore completely ignored, pointing as they do to a powerful God who not only created this universe — but created it for a purpose.

B. THE MYTHS OF EVOLUTION

The basic idea behind the theory of evolution is well known by most people. Almost equally well known are the main events of the emergence of this theory that eventually dominated the scientific world. Such incidents as Darwin thinking about the possibility of evolution on the Galapagos Islands, the first day's 'sell out' of the first edition of his 'Origin of Species' and other well known events appear frequently in books dealing with the history of the rise of the theory. However, investigation of many of these events shows that the popularly held views are quite wrong, and long overdue for correction. The following is a brief refutation of some of the more innaccurate claims that I have examined extensively in another book [26].

   1. 'Darwin first thought about evolution whilst he was on the Galapagos Islands.'

Darwin's actual notebooks made whilst he was on the 'Beagle' voyage have been carefully examined by historians of evolution anxious to discover the development of his thoughts that eventually led him to the theory. They have found that there is not a single word in them that gives any hint of his thinking along such lines. Indeed, the evidence is that he was against such views, for he had studied at university to enter the Church, was a creationist throughout the whole of the voyage and was laughed at by the sailors for quoting the Bible as authoritative during an argument.

Darwin claimed that he first thought of evolution whilst on the Galapagos, but this is not bourne out by his notebooks. He seems to have deliberately done this to bolster his claim that the theory was *his* discovery alone, a position from which he eventually had to retract. Many years before, his grandfather, Erasmus Darwin, had set out all the main ideas, yet Darwin said that he 'got nothing' from him, or from any other scientists, such as Lamarck, who had proposed evolution before Darwin.

When he returned to this country he admitted that, as he was untrained and could not draw, his notes were quite useless; the view also of his 'bulldog', Thomas Henry Huxley. In fact, it was not the animals and plants that Darwin was interested in during his voyage. He concentrated far more on the geology of the continents he visited, his notes being three times larger than those on biological subjects. Indeed, he complained that collecting animals interfered with his geological investigations.

Darwin's very first notes on the theory were not written until ten months after he had returned to this country, and it seems that he had no thoughts on the matter until that time. In trying to discover what could have prompted him into researching evolution, I have examined the relationship that Darwin had with his close friend Charles Lyell. Lyell was the amateur geologist who had already paved the way for evolution by contending that the deposition of the geological strata required vast periods of time. Within a few days of Darwin arriving back in England, Lyell quickly befriended him. I am convinced that it was he who suggested that Darwin should write about evolution. Darwin no doubt knew that were he to do so with some success, it would make him famous, a prospect that he could not resist.

2. 'He carried out a long study of the subject for 23 years (1836 — 1859) before he had gathered enough evidence to prove his theory.'

He wrote his first notes on the theory in 1837. This was followed in 1842 and 1844 by a very full outline of his theory that was sufficiently detailed for them to be published should he die. He then did little more until 1856 when he started a very large work on the whole subject. However, when he received the famous article from Alfred Wallace in 1858, he stopped work on this large work and completed his 'Origin of Species' in the short space of 12 months.

Initially he was greatly involved in producing the official Journal of the Beagle Voyage. He then wrote on the subject of coral reefs and geology, following these with a massive four volume study on barnacles that took him eight years to complete. Thus, far from working on the theory of evolution for twenty three years, he worked for most of the time on other topics.

3. 'The "Origin of Species" was completely sold out on the first day of its publication'.

The publisher, Murray, was prepared to publish Darwin's work when he read the outline of the chapters. However, when he received the complete work, he considered it to be very unscientific and the theory 'absurd'. He furthermore doubted whether it would be a commercial proposition. He was reluctantly persuaded to publish it but he printed only 1,250 copies. These copies were fully subscribed by book dealers who ordered them in batches at the publisher's annual sale, which was a perfectly normal business transaction. Its sales however were unremarkable for both the first and second editions.

Thus, the 'first day's sell out' story is little short of present-day propaganda. It gives the impression that there was a great demand by the public for this revolutionary 'scientific' book of the century, when in reality, it was hardly noticed.

4. 'The Huxley — Wilberforce debate at the British Association meeting in 1860 routed the Bible-believing creationists and was a turning point in the acceptance of the theory.'

Huxley virtually admitted that he attended the British Association meetings in order to further his career. He was an able and extremely ambitious rising young biologist who had difficulty in overcoming the 'Establishment' scientists of his day. He realised however that he could use the newly arising theory of evolution to further his aims.

On the day of the debate, Huxley was intending to leave Oxford, but then changed his mind when reminded of the event. He realised that he might have an opportunity to score a victory over the clergy of the Established Church whom he disliked intensely for their high position in life. Bishop Wilberforce was a very able debater and as Darwin later admitted, highlighted the many weaknesses in the theory. Huxley ignored the scientific evidence and was deliberately rude to the Bishop, accusing him of distorting the arguments and appealing to religious prejudice. To offend a Bishop publicly was unheard of in Victorian times and created quite a scandal. It was this above all else that brought the name of Huxley to the public's attention. The actual debate however was far from going in favour of the evolutionists, a fact recorded by two journalists present.

This meeting has been greatly misreported as a victory for evolution, when in fact it was deliberately used by Huxley to further his ambition. He did this by being publicly offensive to a highly respected Bishop, an act that brought him to the public's attention and is now re-interpreted as a victory for evolution against a reactionary church.

APPENDIX 1 — IS ARCHAEOPTERYX A FAKE?

Much heated discussion followed the claim by Hoyle, Wickramasinghe and others that the fossil, shown in Fig. A1.1, in the possession of the British Museum (Natural History) was fraudulent. The fraud was said to consist of spreading a thin layer of limestone paste on to a slab of rock in which was embedded a genuine fossil, and then imprinting the feathers upon it [1-5]. They claimed that the two surfaces of the split slab did not match exactly as they should have done. These charge were strongly refuted of course by the Natural History Museum [6] who claimed that the two slabs had matching cracks and crystal patterns — a claim the critics dismissed [7].

Having explained their evidence that fraud was involved, the critics asked for a small sample of the material of sufficient size to be examined for artificially applied cementing agents, but this the Museum refused to allow despite several requests. This may seem reasonable, but the Museum itself had removed the slab material in several areas already. The refusal is also in contrast to the extensive tests they were only too happy to carry out on the precious Piltdown fossils when they were intent on proving they were all fraudulent [8p33]. Eventually, after critical reports had been published, two minute samples were provided, but they were insufficient to make a full chemical analysis.

The fossil was photographed using a low angle flash and high resolution colour film that could be greatly enlarged. It would be tedious to list all the criticisms that are made against the genuineness of the fossil, but the following points may be of interest.

i) The discrepancies in the slabs.

The features are fairly clear on the 'main' slab, which is the one most frequently pictured in textbooks. One might have expected the counterslab to be identical as an exact replica in reverse to the main slab, but this is not so. The skeleton is fairly clear, but f the feathers there are only a few faint impressions.

A replica of the two slabs is on display at the Museum, and I can vouch that the differences in the depths of the impressions on the two surfaces is obvious. There may be a reason for this but one would

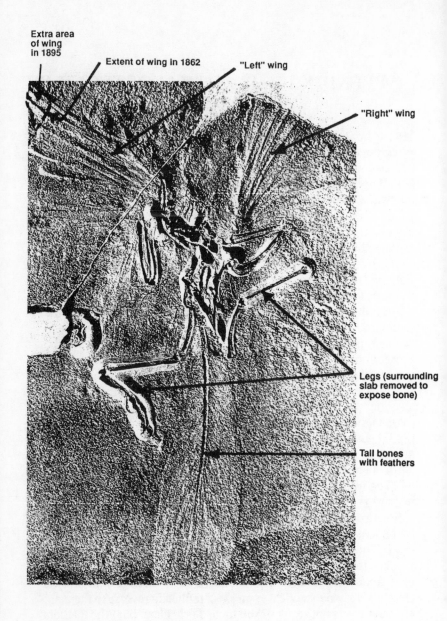

Fig. A1.1 — The main slab.

Fig. A1.2 — The Counterslab

normally expect the two faces to match perfectly. Once the possibility of a forgery is suggested, this striking discrepancy calls for an adequate explanation from the Museum authorities which so far they have failed to provide.

ii) The feather area depression.

The feather impressions are in a depression some 2mm lower than the general slab level. There is no corresponding elevation of the counterslab.

iii) The 'chewing gum blob'.

On the counterslab there is a minute speck of a material that is referred to as 'chewing gum' but which is actually described as 'low-glaze porcelain'. It is suggested that this material once coated the counterslab in order to receive the impressions of the feathers but that it fell off in the process. It was therefore removed by scraping the slab, and marks of brushing and scraping are said to be visible, the small speck of material having survived this process.

iv) The tests.

Two very small samples of the the slab were provided by the museum for testing, one from the slab itself and one from the area of the feathers. Electron microscope examination of the slab material showed characteristics typical of the fine clay of the site in which the fossil was found [7]. The feather sample, however, showed a different material had been added, which the critics claimed was part of the mixture applied to take the impressions of the feathers.

When the results of these tests were presented to the museum, they replied that this additional material was only a preservative coating applied in the past [7p15]. Yet the other slab material did not show these particular inclusions. The critic's report continues —

'This reply also shows a somewhat devious attitude on the part of the Museum. They knew why we wanted the samples and they knew what we were going to do with them. If they knew from the start that the surface of the fossil had been contaminated with preservative, why did they not give us a sample from material slightly under the surface?' [7p15]

v) The Museum's reply.

The Museum claimed that hairline cracks on the slab also appeared across the feathered region, showing that a separate layer had not been applied [6]. The critics claimed that this could have occurred if the slab had moved and the cracks would have appeared through a thin layer placed on the surface [7]. To be fair to the Museum, one would have expected some difference to have been noticed where the hairline crack was in the slab and where it was in a feathered area. Further investigation on this point could be important.

A similar claim was made regarding a dendritic (tree-like) patterns in the slab material. These were formed by dark crystaline growths in a branching pattern, and were visible on both of the slabs. As the patterns corresponded exactly, it was said that this proved that the slabs were matched before they were split, and that there could not therefore be any forgery [6].

The critics agreed that the patterns did match on both the slabs in the areas away from the feathers. It was quite different, however, at the edges of one of the feathered areas. At this location the crystals reach the edge of the feathers, but where you would expect them to continue, in the featherd area there are only a number of dark spots that seem to be protruding through a thin layer of paste. It is this layer of paste that the critics claim was spread over parts of the slab to take the feather impressions. The layer near the edge of the feathers was so thin that the more prominent parts of the crystal pattern actually seemed to be protruding through it. This was the claim of the critics and their enlargements [5p106] of this area certainly appear to support their view.

One photo in the reply by the Museum is of a polished section through the slab. The strange feature is that is shows a thin layer of darker material just below the surface which is said to be an 'impurity .. laid down during sedimentation' [6p623]. Although its thickness of only 500 -850 microns is said to be too thin for artificial feather impressions, it is strange that there should be a thin layer on the surface precisely as claimed by the critics.

vi) The 'white pall'

On a second visit to the museum, when the critics were informed that this would be their last opportunity, they particularly wished to photograph a specific area of the slab. When eventually they were granted access, they found that the area in question was covered by a 'white pall' where a layer of latex rubber had been applied for obtaining casts. That this coating should have been present just when the fossil was to be subjected to another critical examination is a little suspicious to say the least. Strangely, the coating actually enhanced the visibility of a change in the texture which was claimed to add to the proof that the fossil was a forgery.

vii) The extension of the wing area.

By examining early photos and engravings, it was claimed that a small additional area of the wing on the left hand side was exposed between 1862 and 1895, by removing a part of the slab material. The critics explanation for this is a little strange, for they claim that this area of the wing imprint was covered with a thin layer of paste. This was to be removed, proving the fossil was a forgery when the decision to expose the fraud had been reached.

The logic is difficult to follow, for finding imprints of the feathers below what would be taken as parts of the counterslab still clinging to the main slab would surely destroy the charge that the feathers were falsely imprinted.

viii) A dinosaur skeleton?

The fossil does not possess the large keel breast bone of normal birds to which the powerful chest wing muscles are attached. It does however have large crests on the humerus bone to which some think the muscles might have been secured. The main charge, however, is that the skeleton is hardly distinguishable from that of the small dinosaur Compsognathus to which imprints of feathers could have been added.

Following the charge that the fossil was a forgery, a further fossil was discovered that was claimed by Wellnhofer to be another example of Archeopteryx [9]. Found by an amateur in the area where the Berlin and Eichstatt specimens were discovered, he thought it was a Compsognathus skeleton and placed it in his collection. Wellnhofer, however, examined it and commented as follows.

'Under low angle illumination there are distinct parallel impressions originating from the lower arm of the left wing skeleton. These features are interpreted as imprints of feathered shafts. Furthermore, impressions subparallel to the left fingers may mark the outline of the wing. No traces of tail feathers as in the London, Berlin and Eichstatt specimens are visible. Because a question of forgery in the new specimen does not arise, the impressions of the wing feathers are direct evidence that Archeopteryx had feathers.'

In the photograph he gives, there are only a few faint impressions that *might* have been feathers but may simply be natural shallow corrugations in the surface of the rock. They are far from convincing. There is no evidence that the right wing, which is clear of the skeleton, has any feather impressions anywhere near it. It should also be noticed that there were no tail feathers, which weighs heavily against this being an Archeopteryx.

What is interesting is the way in which, in this one short passage, these faint features progress from 'distinct parallel impressions' to being '*interpreted* as imprints of feathered shafts' and finally as '*direct evidence* that Archeopteryx had feathers'. The amount of wishful thinking used in the 'interpretation' is obvious.

The publication of this fairly short article does serve one

purpose. It enables evolutionists to claim, with a confidence that is quite unwarranted, that as another feathered specimen of Archeopteryx has been discovered, the claim that the Museum fossil is a forgery must be groundless. Only when the trouble is taken to examine the claim does it become obvious just how unsupportive even this fossil really is. To make such unjustifiable claims on evidence as inadequate as this can only deepen the suspicion that the main charge of forgery may well be justified.

ix) The ribs.

One biologist, Murris, has pointed out that the rib cage is that of a small reptile, with the ribs attached to the spine in the normal way for a mammal [10]. In birds, however, the lower front half of the ribs articulate with respect to the rear part, which is solidly joined to the spine. As the bird flies, the lower section of the rib cage is swung upwards and forwards by the action of the strong breast muscles used to beat the wings, and the air is pumped through the lungs in the same direction for both the up and the down beat. This could not have taken place with the rib cage of Archaeopteryx, which is yet further evidence that the feathers are an added feature.

x) The acquisition of the fossil.

What is perhaps also of interest is that the area in Germany in which the fossils were found was said to be notorious for the fabrication of 'curios' that the rising gentility liked to display in their collections that were fashionable in those days. The first fossil was discovered in 1867 by Dr. Haberlein, for which he was paid £700 by the British Natural History Museum, a sum that is the equivalent of many hundreds of thousands of pounds today. The second specimen was found by his son, for which he was paid another large sum of money, and which is now in the Berlin Museum.

When the first fossil was discovered, there were hints even then that it may have been a fake. The expert who discovered the fossil of Compsognathus published a paper with the words 'On a new Fossil Reptile supposed to be furnished with Feathers.' Hoyle darkly hints that his death shortly afterwards before he could examine the fossil might have been connected to his criticism of its genuineness.

When the fossil was first displayed in Germany, Haberlein is said to have allowed visitors to glance at it briefly but not to sketch it or examine it closely. This certainly suggests that there was something to hide, and I was reminded of the exact same way in which the Piltdown fossils were kept so carefully guarded by the British Museum. When Dr. L.S.B. Leakey wished to examine the fossil in 1933, he was allowed to compare the originals with a set of casts for a few minutes. The originals were then abrubtly taken away, leaving him only with the casts to examine for the rest of the time [8p33].

xi) The motivation?

Hoyle gives an interesting theory on how the fossil arrived at the Natural History Museum. He conjectures that Owen, a dominant leading member of the Museum and a creationist, willingly bought the fossil for a very high price, even though he had not seen it and may have suspected that it might be a fake even then. The expense took a full two years allowance of the Museum's budget for acquisitions. Owen expected Darwin or Huxley to claim it as strong evidence of an intermediate species, upon which he would expose it as a fraud. On the strength of this, he would then throw out other evidences that supported evolution. Strangely, neither of them referred to this fossil, which one might have expected and which adds to the strangeness of the circumstances surrounding the discovery of this fossil. As a result of the failure to 'rise to the bait', the Museum was left with a fake that it had no opportunity to expose without damaging its own credibility.

As time progressed, the controversial nature of the fossil was forgotten, and as evolutionists took over the Museum, the fossil was used to provide a much needed link between reptiles and birds.

....

The arguments are technical, and it is difficult to say with any certainty at this time where the truth really lies when only photos and documents can be studied.

The book by Hoyle and Wickramasinghe [5] has some excellent photographs but is not particularly clear in its explanations of the more technical details and charges they are making. It is, however, far more convincing than the single paper published by the Museum staff which is quite insufficient as a defence against the serious charges concerning the precious relic of which they are the guardians. Their refusal to allow any further examination of the fossil is in itself a cause for questioning their reason for guarding it so carefully. Until the fossil can be thoroughly examined by a number of experts, the onus still lies on them to prove that it is not a fake.

It would be interesting if the controversy were to be revitalised, but I feel that the authorities are hoping that the whole subject will quietly fade away. Another scandal of the size of Piltdown would once again make the Museum the laughing stock of both the scientific world and of the community at large.

As is often the case, it is the 'side effects' that can be as revealing as the main dispute.

Hoyle was once famous for his work in astronomy. Later, however, he made the controversial proposal that as the complex molecules needed for primitive life could not possibly have formed on earth, they must have come from outer space. This was more than sufficient for him to be classed as a scientific heretic, and he gave an amusing instance of the degree to which he was subsequently ostracised by his professional colleagues. He recounted that he 'had sat for 20 minutes in a dentists waiting room in total silence while the other occupant, a distinguished scientist and a former friend, held a magazine just a few inches from his nose in terror of being drawn into conversation with the infidel!' [11].

One other passage occasioned mild amusement. This was in the Museum's defence of the fossil, in the course of which the importance of removing doubts from the mind of the public and of students of zoology regarding the authenticity of the fossil was emphasised. The report continued —

> '*More important still*, we must put the record straight because of the Creationists, who are interested in any new ideas that, implicitly or explicitly, appear to threaten the concept of evolution.' [6p623]

The order of priorities of the Museum staff is therefore clear. Ensuring that creationists are not allowed to get even a fingerhold on any such evidence against their fiercely guarded theory of evolution is actually placed *above* the interest of disseminating the truth to the public and students of zoology. The senior staff of the British Natural History Museum are members of a powerful and prestigious organisation. That they should be so concerned by the activities of a handful of these misguided creationists surely indicates how aware they are of the fragility of the evolutionary foundations upon which they rest.

BIBLIOGRAPHY

1   Trop, M. 'Is Archaeopteryx a Fake?' Creation Science Research Quarterly v20 n2 p121-2 September 1983.

2   Watkins, R. S., Hoyle, F. et al 'Archaeopteryx — a Photographic Study' British Journal of Photography, 8 March 1985 p264-6

3   Watkins, R. S., Hoyle, F. et al 'Archaeopteryx — a further comment' British Journal of Photography 29 March 1985 p358-9 and 367.

176

Science vs Evolution

4   Watkins, R. S., Hoyle, F. et al 'Archaeopteryx — further evidence' British Journal of Photography 26 April 1985 p468-470

5   Hoyle, F. and Wickramasinghe, C. 'Archaeopteryx, the Primordial Bird: A Case of Fossil Forgery' Pub. C. Davies, Sketty, Swansea, 1986.

6   Charig, A. et al. 'Archaeopteryx is not a Forgery' Science v232 n4750 p622-626, 2 May 1986.

7   Spetner, L.M., Hoyle, F. et al 'Archaeopteryx — more evidence of a forgery' British Journal of Photography 7 January 1988 p14-17

8   Bowden, M., 'Ape-men — Fact or Fallacy ?' 2nd enlarged edition, Sovereign Publications 1981

9   Wellnhofer, P. 'A New Specimen of Archeopteryx' Science v240 p1790-2 24 June 1988.

10   Murris, H., 'Archeopteryx: vat vol Tegenstrygdigheden (A Barrel full of Contradictions)' Bijbel en Wetenschap, June 1990, n134 p143-147.

11   The Mail on Sunday, October 23, 1983 p6.

APPENDIX 2 — THE PILTDOWN HOAX — FURTHER REVELATIONS

The fossils of this notorious fraud were discovered in the years 1908 — 1915 in Sussex. The main ones consisted of a few pieces of human skull, an ape's jawbone and a canine tooth, together with several stone artefacts and fossillised animal remains. The reconstructed skull was accepted as a genuine link and numerous papers were written about it by experts for many years.

All of the discoveries were found to be fraudulent in 1953. An orangutan's jaw bone had been broken and stained, and the teeth had been filed to make them look like an animal half way between man and ape. The culprit usually blamed for this hoax is a local lawyer, Charles Dawson. However, careful investigation of all the evidence exonerates Dawson and points strongly towards the Jesuit priest Teilhard de Chardin, who helped with the excavations for the fossils, as being the principal hoaxer. The reader is pointed to reference 5 for the full evidence in support of this accusation, and the background to what follows below.

FURTHER REVELATIONS.

In 1978, there was renewed interest in the Piltdown fraud, when an accusation was made that Prof. Sollas was the man who provided the technical know-how in the perpetration of the fraud. In the course of the furore, Dr. L.B. Halstead suggested that the British Natural History Museum staff had a hand in it, for he wrote a letter that was published in the Times on November 25th in which he said —

> 'There is evidence that the medieval orangutan lower jaw which made up the Piltdown jaw came from the Natural History Museum itself and was provided by Dr. M.A.C. Hinton (a former Keeper of Zoology). Indeed, according to Hinton himself the Piltdown man hoax was initially planned and executed within the Museum.
> 'The current scenario would seem to be one of an extensive conspiracy involving Hinton, a few other colleagues in the Museum, with Teilhard de Chardin contributing a Tunisian elephant tooth and the "missing" canine. The expertise involved in the Piltdown hoaxes still assuredly points to Sollas.'

Since the writing of 'Ape-men — Fact or Fallacy?' there have been several books and articles written to prove that Dawson's expert help came from some other person. These include such names as Lewis Abbot (a local collector), Dr. S. Woodhead (a chemist friend of Dawson), and Sir Arthur Conan Doyle. Apart from the American Stephen J. Gould, no-one else has supported the case against Teilhard de Chardin. They have indeed gone to great lengths to protect his name from any possible implication in the fraud, and consistently emphasise Dawson's 'guilt'.

SPENCERS' INVESTIGATION

The most recent claim to have found (yet again) the 'real' perpetrator of the fraud has been made by Dr. Frank Spencer who accuses Sir Arthur Keith [1 and 2]. Keith had made a reconstruction of the skull shortly after the fossils had been discovered. On the evidence Spencer presents, the case against Keith being the mastermind behind the plot is thin indeed. That he may have been aware that the discoveries were indeed fraudulent is difficult to prove, but from my reading I think that even this is very unlikely.

The two volume work that Spencer has produced is very thorough and meticulously documented, and it is in the fresh information he presents that the real interest lies. The first volume gives the history of the hoax and looks at various suspects before dismissing them. As is often found in examining defensive works such as these, however, the evidence they present regarding those whom the writer seeks to eliminate, actually points to their complicity in the hoax. I will simply give some of the evidence that confirms my original accusations in my earlier book, and then continue with showing that a concerted operation was mounted to incriminate Dawson even before the hoax was said to have been first suspected.

1) Martin Hinton.

a) Hinton is considered as a possible suspect, and several pages are devoted to his activities. He was still alive when the fraud was exposed, and rushed off a letter to the Times in which he sought to exonerate himself. He claimed that had he 'handled' the jaw and the tooth, ' ... they would have been referred without hesitation to the Chimpanzee' [1p149]. Yet earlier in the same letter he notes that he saw them in a showcase, and on one occasion he 'got within handling distance..and then did not handle them.'

He hardly needed to hold them in his hands in order to see that they were fakes. Others pointed out that Smith-Woodward had permitted many visitors to inspect them fully, and as Hinton was working at the Natural History Museum at that time, he would surely have had an opportunity to make a full inspection. His letter, in fact, is so palpably inconsistent that even the experts considered that he did his case little good by writing it.

His double-mindedness is seen by an article he wrote in 1926 in which says 'Eoanthropus [the official name for the Piltdown fossils] himself is surely as primitive a mammal as one could wish to find … ' [1p177]. He thus endorses these fossils which he was to later say he would have classified as fraudulent had he been allowed to inspect them closely.

b) He is said to have written to a friend ' …not to pay too much attention to the finds … '. When asked about this, Hinton neither denied nor confirmed the story. Spencer comments that 'To have admitted the existence of this letter would have made him an accesary after the fact' [1p178].

c) He also told a friend, John Irving; a BBC producer, that he believed the perpetrator had been working at the British Museum at the time of the hoax, and that he was unable to reveal his name because he was still alive [1p178]. Spencer comments; 'To some this amounted to a confession, others believed that his reference to the forger being alive at the time of the unmasking was a red herring, and that he was really pointing, indirectly, to Woodward.'

Why he should not openly accuse Woodward who had died several years before, is incomprehensible, and therefore it is far more likely to be an indirect form of confession.

d) When Hinton was interviewed about the fraud he suggested that the material had been imported 'possibly from Montpellier' [1p150]. This seems to have been a pointed implication of Teilhard's direct involvement in the fraud. He later retracted this saying that it was 'a pure spur of the moment guess'. How one can name a specific town and then call it 'a pure guess' I frankly fail to see.

e) Lord Zuckerman's review.

The very thin evidence Spencer produced to support his case against Sir Arthur Keith was strongly criticised by Lord Zuckerman in The New York Review of Books (8 November 1990). More interesting, however, was Zuckerman's view of who the culprit really was. He claimed this was Martin Hinton, the same person that Halstead had pointed to twelve years previously.

I quote Zuckerman's passage on this.

'Dr. Spencer removes Hinton from his extraordinary list of possible suspects for two main reasons: first, because had the fraud been

discovered it would have ruined his chances of getting a paid job at the museum; and second, because if his attempt to make a fool of Smith-Woodward [Keeper of the Geological Department at the Museum, and a worker with Dawson at the Piltdown site] had been found out, he would have delivered "a devastating blow to the credibility" of a group of fossil hunters of which he was a member.'

I would comment on two points in this passage.

i) Hinton was a member of a closely knit *group* of 'fossil hunters', and any accusation of fraud against him would have brought down the credibility of them all. The actual group Spencer refers to is the Ightham Circle of amateur fossil hunters in Kent, who were active at the time of the Piltdown discoveries. I think that it is very unlikely that they had anything to do with the hoax despite this being suggested by some.

By far the more important group that would have been brought down would have been those within the Museum, such as Hinton himself, and others closely connected to the fraud such as Teilhard de Chardin, possibly Sollas and others whose identity may yet be revealed. Also included in this network are two other groups. The first would be those who have consistently engaged in the protection of the fraudulent fossils during their long acceptance as valuable relics. The second would be the instigators of the elaborate cover-up to ensure that the real culprits would not be exposed after the fraud was 'discovered'. I will examine this aspect later.

I (and Halstead) have maintained that the Piltdown Fraud was not the work of one individual, but of several experts well placed both inside and outside the British Natural History Museum. This is the only explanation that can be given for the successful concealment of the hoax from other scientists and the general public for forty one years.

ii) I do not believe that the hoax was ever perpetrated simply to 'make a fool of Sir Arthur Smith-Woodward'. As Spencer points out, (and Zuckerman fails to answer satisfactorily), had the fraud been discovered, it would have destroyed any chance of Hinton being offered a career in the Museum. Furthermore, the rising careers of others would also have come crashing down. Risks such as these would have far outweighed the temporary pleasure of fooling the autocratic Smith-Woodward. It can only be concluded that it was a carefully planned conspiracy by several experts to provide badly needed evidence of the evolution of man from ape ancestors. The consistent claim that it was 'to fool Smith-Woodward' is only a smokescreen to hide the real intention of the perpetrators, which was to fool the public regarding the supposed existence of 'ape-men'.

f) Spencer notes that 'Both Weiner's and Oakley's files are filled with notes and correspondence relating to Hinton and the charge that he and some of his Ightham associates conspired to fabricate the Piltdown forgery. While much of this material makes stimulating reading it too must ultimately be seen as gossip' [1p175].

One may be left with the suspicion that what is dismissed as 'gossip' might possibly be information that it would be unwise to reveal. Despite the activities of Hinton and the various accusations against him, no final verdict of his complicity or exoneration regarding the fraud is given, for Spencer seems to leave this question unanswered.

2. Teilhard de Chardin.

Spencer's account of how Teilhard was interviewed, not only further implicates him in the fraud, but casts doubt on those who cross examined him about his part in the discoveries as to whether they were really intent upon revealing the truth.

There was an exchange of letters between Oakley and Teilhard when the fraud was discovered, in which Teilhard's replies 'became increasingly defensive' [1p183]. Eventually Teilhard came to England to see Weiner and Oakley in 1954, presumably to make his 'confession' as one person put it. The interview was far from satisfactory, for Teilhard was evasive in the extreme, trying to deflect the discussion to his work in Africa. At one stage he denied that he knew Dawson very well as a person. Yet he had stayed with him for several days over a period of time when the excavations were progressing. He also 'avoided answering some of Edward's questions by turning to Oakley' [2p250]

During this same visit, Teilhard tried to minimise the part he played by saying 'I was a mere youth at the time, little more than a boy' [2p248]. Yet in 1912 he was 24 years old!

Spencer acknowledges that Teilhard is 'a highly attractive candidate' but seeks to exonerate him by adding that as a young priest he would have had little chance to prepare his materials at the seminary. He adds 'He could of course have had outside help — but who? Was it possible that he had been Dawson's accomplice?'

Gould's evidence against Teilhard is dismissed, saying 'his case ultimately boils down to little more than an informed opinion … ' In this he seems as keen as most other investigators to exonerate the most likely suspect. Spencer suggests that Teilhard's reticence was due to not wanting to be involved in the hoax by implication, and therefore he 'evidently decided that the most expedient (as well as the most honourable) course of action was to say nothing' [1p187].

Yet again, Teilhard is sheltered from any complicity in the plot by the Establishment figures.

3. Essex.

Robert Essex was a teacher in the area, and mixed with Dawson and Teilhard. When the fraud was announced, Essex went to the Museum in January 1954, and was interviewed by Oakley and Edwards. His evidence is made to look ridiculous, however, for Spencer recounts — 'Nearly stone deaf and wearing an inefficient hearing aid, Essex had surfaced [note the derogatory implications of this description] at the British Museum (Natural History) early in January 1954 anxious to tell his story' [1p150]. Edwards reported to Weiner that 'Most of his supposed evidence was elaborate surmise. He was pretty hopeless at dates ... '

Spencer continues

'Essex believed Dawson had been an innocent victim, duped by a conniving French cleric. While the details of Essex's seemingly preposterous story did not hold together, Weiner did not dismiss completely the possibility of Teilhard's involvement' [1p151].

Although elsewhere Spencer and others admit that Teilhard was a prime suspect, Essex's first-hand evidence is dismissed as 'seemingly preposterous'.

Essex wrote an article in which he gave his evidence on the Piltdown fraud that appeared in the 'Kent and Sussex Journal' in 1955. In this he gave his evidence against a Mr. X, whom I identified as being Teilhard, which is confirmed by Spencer. I reproduced the article in my 'Ape' book on pages 48-50. Very much to my surprise, Spencer commented that Essex's article is to be found in 'Bowden 1978' in the references.

4. Weiner and Miss Kenward.

When the investigation of the fraud was in progress but before it was publicised, Dr. J.S. Weiner visited the Piltdown area, asking the locals a number of questions. He also twice interviewed Miss Mabel Kenward, who, as a young woman, was living at Barkham Manor when the fossils were found there. I interviewed Miss Kenward, who said that on his first visit, Weiner (accompanied by Prof. G.A. Harrison) was particularly keen to know if any of the original workmen who had found the first fossils of the skull (which they mistook for a 'coconut') were still alive, but none were. He also visited other locals, paying handsomely for any information about the circumstances in which the finds had been made, and any gossip about Dawson.

It was important for the case against Dawson that the skull pieces, the first discoveries made by him, should also be shown to be fraudulent. This would enable Dawson to be implicated before anyone else — particularly Smith-Woodward and Teilhard de Chardin — appeared on the scene. If the skull, however, was genuine, then all the later fakes could have been placed by others. Weiner brought as much evidence as he could to show that the skull was indeed faked also, and claimed that the 'coconut' story 'sinks into oblivion'. Dawson, being then the only one involved in the discovery of the 'fake' skull pieces was thereby made to be the only suspect who fitted all the evidence.

Mabel Kenward also told me that when Weiner made the second visit, accompanied by several other people, she accused Weiner and Harrison of coming to see her some time before the present interview. Weiner, however, flatly denied this. Having recorded all that Miss Kenward had told me, I was reluctant to publicise her account of what took place, as the evidence could not be corroborated. She also mentioned that her friend, Francis Vere, had been threatened with a libel action if he were to print anything defamatory — a situation I was not keen to enter in to.

Weiner's strenuous efforts to implicate Dawson were vigorously rebutted by Miss Kenward, who was a personal friend of Dawson, and she asked Francis Vere to write in his defence. His subsequent books 'The Piltdown Fantasy' [3A] and 'Lessons from Piltdown' [3B] are an excellent defence of Dawson, a critique of Weiner's evidence and an exposure of the gullibility (which I would suggest is the right word to describe their approach) of many scientific 'experts'.

When the discovery of the fraud was at long last made public in November 1953, Miss Kenward wrote directly to Weiner on 1st July 1954, emphasising that the skull was found in *hard* (i.e. undisturbed) gravel [2p246]. Weiner replied that 'Charles Dawson had stressed over and over again that a great deal of the gravel was loose at all times when the pieces of cranium came to light. He describes how these pieces were found in 'spoil heaps'. There is little doubt that during the time that Woodward was engaged in the excavations, as well as before, the gravel was, to use Dawson's expression, in a "disturbed" condition.' [1p247]

Miss Kenward was stung into a sharp response, and replied on the 4th July 1954 —

'I take great exception to your letter of the 3rd inst. in reply to mine to you. In the letter you definitely imply that I am lying when I tell you the ground where the cranium of the Piltdown skull was dug, had not been uncovered before. My father — man of the highest integrity saw his workmen strike with a pick the skull which was lying buried in untouched gravel, and thereby shattering it in all directions. I have nothing to say about the subsequent finds, which it has been claimed had been "planted" ... I also resent very much that you came last spring and questioned me about Mr. Dawson without telling me the object of your visit ... ' [2p247]

I will be referring to this last sentence later.

In 1955, Weiner published his book on the fraud [4], which again prompted Miss Kenward to write a letter to the Daily Telegraph who printed it on 23rd February 1955 (the Times refused to publish it). She again specifically states that the skull was first discovered 'in unmoved gravel' by the workmen who gave a piece to Dawson when he later came to the Manor.

Thus, despite all the evidence of a witness actually present at the site, and the confirmation of others living at the time of their discovery, Weiner nevertheless insisted that the skull pieces, *were fakes* planted by Dawson in loose gravel.

Weiner's first visit to Piltdown

Ever since I had interviewed Miss Kenward, and even after a first reading of Spencer's two large books, I was still a little puzzled why Weiner should so flatly deny that he had visited her at an earlier time. Why should this be so significant or important to be worth denying? It was only when I later read of the timing of certain events that the importance of Weiner's reaction became clear.

The scenario Weiner presents, and which Spencer repeats is that Weiner was one of a number who attended a conference, organised by Kenneth Oakley, in London on 27th July 1953 [1p133]. In the afternoon of the 30th, the delegates were taken to the Geology Department where, amongst other things, they were allowed to handle the original Piltdown fossils. Later that evening, Weiner was dining with Oakley and Washburn, when he learned from Oakley that the reason that the Piltdown II site (where some other fossils had been found) had never been excavated, was because 'it had quite possibly been known only to Dawson' [1p135].

This seems to have greatly worried Weiner, and he graphically records how he spent a troubled night, conjecturing whether the fossils could be fraudulent. In the next few days he proceeded to file and stain a chimpanzee's teeth and found that they could be made to look surprisingly like the Piltdown teeth.

Spencer records, 'Having spent the better part of a week mulling over his thesis', Weiner eventually went to his professor, Le Gros Clark, who, because of 'the sensitive nature of Weiner's hypothesis, it was agreed that Oakley should be contacted by telephone rather than letter'. Oakley was 'taken aback by the call from Oxford' but 'said he would review the materials and call back', which he did the same day. Weiner remembered 'that he was utterly convinced that artificial abrasion had been applied' and that it 'was obvious on the canine'. 'Oakley also agreed that the British Museum should be actively involved in the exposure, but that in the interim the entire matter should be kept secret' [1p137].

This phone call was clearly the crucial event when the experts agreed that the fraud should be exposed, and according to the footnote, it was on the 6th August.

Turning to the dates of Weiner's (and Harrison's) visits to Piltdown, confirmation that Weiner made two visits is given by Spencer. He says,

'The timing of Weiner's first visit to Piltdown is uncertain. Although a later letter from Mabel Kenward suggests that it had been in the spring [see above] (prior to the London Conference …)[on 30th July] this seems unlikely. Prof. Geoffrey A. Harrison (Oxford University) who assisted Weiner in his enquiries is convinced the first visit had been towards the end of July or the beginning of August (personal communication).' [2p217]

It seems to me a little surprising that intelligent and busy men, as well as official establishments, do not appear to have kept a diary, if only to record future engagements. Reference to someones 1953 diary would surely have clarified the precise dates of their visits. Harrison's memory is surely faulty, for according to the official scenario, Weiner did not mention to anyone else his suspicions until the 6th August. If therefore the *first* visit could have been as late as 'the beginning of August', let us say that this might have been about the 8th August, as it could not surely from his account have been much later, *then within say two to four days after the famous phone call, Weiner and Harrison were in Piltdown interviewing people.* This would indicate almost indecent haste to find a culprit, *even before the experiments to prove that it was a forgery had got underway.*

I cannot but come to the conclusion that the whole of the sequence of events given by Weiner, Harrison and Spencer are not an accurate record. In trying to determine the true course of events, I would present the following points.

   i) **The original fossils.**
Woodward appears to have allowed free access to the original fossils to many experts, but this does not seem to have continued after his death. I have recorded that even top experts, such as Louis

Leakey, were not allowed to examine the *original* fossils for more than a few minutes, being left after this time with only accurate casts [5p33]. This would have prevented them from noticing any suspicious features such as the painting of the canine with Vandyke Brown paint, abrasion marks made by filing the teeth etc. Yet at the London Conference in 1953, the museum staff allowed them to be handled by numerous experts freely. This suggests that a change of policy regarding allowable access to the fossils had already been decided upon at some stage.

ii) The fraudulent nature of the fossils.

When Oakley received the 6th August telephone call, he phoned back later the same day, reporting that he was convinced that 'artificial abrasion had been applied.' Now these fossils had been in the possession of the Natural History Museum for some 40 years. Are we to believe that during that time, not one single scientist had ever examined them closely and seen these obvious signs of artificial abrasion, which Oakley is said to have detected within a matter of hours?

But the possibility of the fossils being fraudulent was not too difficult to detect. Oakley himself mentioned that in a book he published in 1949 'I risked hinting that the "bone implement" was a forgery' [2p199]. If he had his suspicions as early as that, why did he not pursue them further? Yet on receiving the famous phone call that the fossils might be faked 'he was taken aback'. He also noted in 1950 that the teeth 'have been slightly abraided by the river sand' [2p192]. But an electron microscope picture [1p138] clearly shows scratch marks all fairly parallel to each other, which are hardly what would be expected from random scratches from sand in a stream.

In 1951, Oakley, in referring to the coating on the canine, said it was 'obscured by a thin film of iron oxide, and it is difficult to remove this without producing a surface which was largely artificial' [2p193]. When the fraud was exposed, the canine had been coated with paint, probably Vandyke Brown, to make it match the colour of the other fossils. Were our experts unable to tell the difference between iron oxide and a coat of paint?

In the official report, it was claimed that the whole fraud was 'extraordinarily skilful' [1p141]. Examination of the evidence proving the fraud, however, shows that in some cases it should have been patently obvious to anyone making a very close inspection. It is little wonder that the exposure brought considerable ridicule upon the whole of the scientific establishment at the Museum.

iii) Knowledge of the fraud.

That some or all of the Piltdown fossils were fraudulent was being expressed even during their discovery. Morris, Woodhead and others seem to have had reservations regarding the authenticity of the finds. Hinton, Kennard and Corner all appear to have known quite definitely that they were fakes. Even the American expert Gregory who had visited England in 1913, had written as early as 1914 'It has been suspected by some that.. they may even be a deliberate hoax' [2p103]. As we have seen, Oakley himself had reservations about the genuineness of the teeth and the 'bone implement'.

With all these indications, are we to believe that not a single one of the Museum authorities ever had the slightest hint that Piltdown was a hoax? Surely not. I would repeat my contention that they were well aware of this, and eventually chose their own time and procedure to expose it as a fact publicly.

iv) The early first visit.

Finally, we have the testimony of Miss Kenward, that she was interviewed in the Spring of 1953 by Weiner and Harrison. She wrote that letter in 1954, when she was 69, and would have had a clear memory of the approximate date of the first visit that would have taken place only one year before. When I interviewed her in 1976 she was quite articulate and clear in her mind, and from notes that I made at the time, emphasised that this was *before* the fraud was publicised. I therefore consider her account as accurate and trust-worthy, i.e. that she *was* visited in the Spring of 1953 and not in 'early August'.

Now Weiner claimed that he first thought of the fraud on the 30th July 1953. There were only two visits by both Weiner and Harrison to Piltdown. The first was said to be 'the end of July or early August' [1p141 and 1p230 note 34]. The second visit was said to have been made 'a week later' after that, i.e. about the 15th August [1p141 and 1p230 note 36]. Now if this is correct, why should Weiner have denied that he had seen Miss Kenward only two weeks before then? It should have been fresh in both their memories and Weiner had no reason whatsoever to contradict her claim.

There is one simple explanation which I would propose that would explain his concern. This is that his first meeting with Miss Kenward was not just a week before, but 'in the Spring', as she claimed later in her letter. Weiner *had* to deny this early date because it was long before the date of July 30th which is when he claimed he first thought of the possibility of a fraud.

If this is the case, then Weiner was scouring Piltdown long before he claims his first thought of forgery occurred to him on the 30th July 1953. This would explain the vagueness of the date of the first visit, for this had to be re-dated to 'late July or early August'. To have given the correct date would have exposed the fact that a cover-up operation was already being investigated long before Weiner's 'troubled night' of the 30th July.

It is probably then that the (second) 'official' interview of Miss Kenward took place about the 15th August, at which she accused Weiner and Harrison of having visited her before 'in the Spring'. When Weiner denied this, she was naturally infuriated.

I would therefore suggest that quite some time before the London Conference in July, it had been decided that the fossils were to be exposed as a fake. As it was important that the professionals involved in the original discoveries should be protected from any accusation of complicity in the fraud, Weiner went around Piltdown well in advance of any publicity being set in motion. He specifically checked to see if any of the original diggers at the pit were still living, but none were. Indeed, when I interviewed Miss Kenward she told me that 'Weiner had gone round the area saying, "Here's a shilling if you can tell me anything about the Piltdown discoveries", and they had told him all sorts of things to get the money.'

It was only when the fraud was publicised much later that Miss Kenward first became aware that his innocent questioning of her in the Spring of 1953 (and possibly the second interview also) about the discoveries were to be used to incriminate her friend Dawson. She realised that she had been duped by Wiener about his real intentions, and this drew the sharp rebuke at the end of her letter of the 4th July 1954.

Presumably, after Weiner's first visit, when it was felt that there was sufficient room for ensuring that Dawson could be used as a scapegoat for all or most of the blame, only then was the machinery to publicise the fraud put into motion. Was this the purpose of the evening meeting after the Conference on the 30th July?

[I would here mention a further unjust accusation that Weiner used to blacken Dawson's character, which unfortunately is frequently repeated in books about Piltdown. Weiner claimed that he was given 'a precise account' by a Mr. Salzmann, a member of the Sussex Archaeological Society, that they had asked Dawson to act on their behalf to purchase Castle Lodge where they met and had a small museum. When they found that he had purchased it himself they 'were taken aback'. The implication was that Dawson was prepared to use underhand tactics to get what he wanted.

Yet in a letter in the Sunday Times on 23rd January 1955, Salzmann said that Weiner's statement that the association had asked Dawson to act on their behalf was 'completely untrue.' Vere, who related this incident, observed

' ... it was not for Weiner to find fault with scientists who do not accurately report what they hear. If his preconceptions caused Weiner to misunderstand what was said to him at first hand, what possible reliance can you place on his reports of what other people told him other people said?' [3Bp19]]

The timing of the exposure

What was it that triggered the decision to publicise the fraud?

In 1949 Oakley carried out some Fluorine tests on the skull and jaw and found them to have the same date but later than expected, and less than some of the other animal bones. When writing about this much later in 1976 he said that his 'instinctive reaction was to regard Eoanthropus as bogus'. In addition, the whiteness of the drillings from the teeth should have aroused his suspicions [5p31].

When Oakley gave a lecture on these Fluorine tests in 1950, Weiner claimed that he spoke to Oakley saying that the Fluorine levels of the fossil skull and jaw were too low and therefore the date was too young for man to have an ape-like jaw [8]. Apparently, Oakley did not seem to be impressed for 'he took the matter no further.' Yet as we have seen, he claimed that when he discussed the bone implement he had suggested it might have been fraudulent. There appears to be a discrepancy here.

I consider that the Museum authorities were actually well aware that the fossils were fraudulent even from the date of their discovery. It may have been the publicising of Oakley's Fluorine tests in 1950, and Weiner pointing out that the dating was now too young, that prompted them to hide the fact no longer. Others outside the Museum might well now ask some awkward questions and it was essential that the 'exposure' should be fully under their control. It could therefore be from this time that the planning started, and not from Weiner's 'troubled' night in 1953 after the London meeting.

Having, I trust, given sufficient evidence to show that the preliminary stages of the exposure of the hoax were not in accordance with the story presented to the public, and that the whole sequence of the unfolding of the events was carefully pre-planned, I will leave the rest to the imagination of the reader.

The cover-up of Teilhard's involvement

I have consistently maintained that the most striking feature that runs as a thread throughout all of my examination of this hoax is the constant protection of Teilhard from having any proven involvement in it, and the insistence that Dawson was the principle hoaxer.

That the protection of Teilhard's name is still continuing can be seen by a remark made by Spencer, that not only shows up his position, but the reluctance of the investigators to question Teilhard too closely. Spencer relates how

' ... everyone concerned with these investigations, including Weiner, was puzzled by Teilhard's attitude. In spite of repeated attempts by Oakley to get answers to specific questions, the Frenchman's replies had been evasive as well as contradictory on a number of details. Indeed at one point he even denied being a close friend of Dawson. Was he simply embarrassed by the whole affair?'

After quoting a letter from Le Gros Clark critical of Teilhard, Spencer then terminates this digression about Teilhard with the note—

'Unable to advance the case against Teilhard, Weiner's attention shifted back to Marriot and Morris' [1p151]

Here then we have a situation where a principle suspect is contradicting himself, is evasive and telling half lies. What do all of the intelligent and highly paid experts who have questioned him several times then do? Do they redouble their efforts in trying to find out from him the real truth? No: They simply look elsewhere!

I am wondering how long a detective would last in his position were he to extend the same treatment to the biggest suspect in a case of serious fraud? Having found that he was evasive, contradictory and acting in a very uncooperative way, would he therefore give up and 'shift his attention' to other less likely suspects? The whole way in which Teilhard is treated so cautiously by the establishment cannot but raise the suspicion that they were well aware of the true identity of the hoaxer. Certainly, no firm evidence against him was allowed to be publicised.

If this is correct, as I would suggest it is, then all those involved in protecting Teilhard cannot avoid being tainted with some degree of guilt in the elaborate cover-up that was set in motion at a very early stage of the Museum's investigations of the hoax.

Costello's accusations.

One of the personalities accused of being behind the fraud is Samuel Woodhead, a local chemistry teacher and Public Analyst who helped Dawson in the very early stages of the finding of the true skull pieces. The accusation that he was the main perpetrator of the hoax was made by the writer Mr. Peter Costello. Following a letter of mine that appeared in the Daily Telegraph on 2nd November 1978, we corresponded for a while, and eventually met locally. We discussed our mutual certainty of Teilhard's involvement, during which he mentioned that he had carefully researched this, even to the extent of checking local Sussex timetables of the period to show that Teilhard could have caught a train to leave Piltdown and reach his Seminary in time on a certain day.

In 1985 I was greatly surprised to see that he was now accusing Woodhead and not Teilhard [6]. Indeed he had written that 'there was no evidence at all of his complicity'. I wrote to him in July 1987 asking what the evidence was that made him shift his interest, and that I was awaiting his book on the subject. He assured me that more information was arriving, but at this date of writing (early 1991), the book has still not appeared. Spencer considers Costello's case against Woodhead is inadequate, with which I would agree.

In discussing Costello's accusation against Woodhead as the hoaxer, Spencer quotes his biographer as saying Woodhead was 'a deeply religious man whose every action was governed by his Christian beliefs'. Spencer than comments 'Costello has interpreted this to mean he was a religious fanatic (inferring that he might well have been a closet creationist)' [1p237 note 82].

If Woodhead was a sincere Christian he is hardly likely to have engaged in a deceitful hoax against anyone, particularly his close friend Dawson, but this does not appear to have occurred to either Costello or Spencer. Also amusing is the sense of shock they display on making the 'logical' sequence of connections that a true Christian = a religious fanatic = a secret creationist = a man to be abhorred! If he were a creationist, he is hardly likely to have had a hand in creating a false link between man and apes — but again this simple contradiction does not seem to have struck either of our two writers.

The net spreads wider

What was of greater interest to me in a further article Costello wrote [7] was the connections he found between some of the suspects, which I will briefly set out.

Dr. John Hewitt, Professor Emeritus of Chemistry at Queen Mary's College, admitted to friends in 1952 that he was responsible with others for the hoax.

In 1898 Hewitt had worked with Woodhead and Dawson on the investigations of some natural gas at Heathfield. He also served on the same Council of the Society of Public Analysts as Woodhead, and possibly through this connection heard of Dawson's discovery of skull pieces at Piltdown long before the news became public knowledge.

Hewitt said he had the help of one other person who later withdrew, who was replaced by another, both of whom appeared to be fellow academics. He was an undergraduate at St. John's College, Cambridge, the same college attended by Prof. Sollas, Sir Grafton Elliot Smith and Louis Leakey. Cambridge is often mentioned by different investigators as having some implication in the plot. What is of particular interest is that Hewitt was a friend of Ralph Meldola whom Costello claims was 'the authority on evolution and a fellow chemist.' Meldola was a member of the Essex field club, one of whose members was Martin Hinton, whose likely complicity in the hoax we have examined above.

I have no evidence to prove it, but I would suggest that it is possible that Meldola may have been the initiator of the hoax and acted as the central figure who would coordinate other conspirators in their respective parts. He would doubtless be keen to further the theory of evolution on which he was an authority, and any new evidence in its favour would be more than welcome. The bones of Java Man were still controversial and therefore discovery of another link between man and ape would be an enormous vindication of the theory. He had connections with Hewitt, other academics and particularly Martin Hinton in the Natural History Museum and therefore seems to have been well placed to have fulfilled this role. He had the motive and was in a prime position to instigate just such a 'seeding' of a likely site as he would have heard was arising at Piltdown.

The principle member of the group of forgers who would be responsible for placing the false material at the site was undoubtably Teilhard de Chardin, but I have not come across any clear evidence of direct links between him and other likely members of the conspiracy. This, however, is not a major obstacle, for clandestine connections could have been easily available.

In two papers (1911 and 1913) by Woodward, Dawson had paid tribute to Teilhard's help. He was therefore known to the authorities at the Museum. Whether he had any personal contact with the staff apart from Sir Arthur Smith-Woodward I have no knowledge. He also had very wide ranging connections with communists [5p119], a drug smuggler [5p233] and seems to have unobstructed access to the very highest academic circles in many countries. There can be little doubt that he was a member of a very influential circle with connections world-wide which I have referred to elsewhere [5p153-

4]. What might this circle have been? There are several that he may have used.

There is in this country at least (and it would be duplicated overseas), what I have referred to as The Establishment — those members of our society who are the intelligensia and leaders of the land who control many of the appointments to senior positions of influence. Acceptance by this circle can result in introductions to many powerful interests. There is also Freemasonry, with similar or parallel contacts throughout the world. It should also not be forgotten that Teilhard was a Jesuit, an organisation that over the years has earned a notorious reputation for its devious intrigues. Finally, if some writers are to be believed, there is the nebulous but very powerful organisation of the Illuminati whose connections straddle the world.

[As an indication of the wide range of support that he still receives, often from unexpected quarters, I have before me as a write a press release publicising the 'Teilhard de Chardin Centenary Exhibition' held in July 1983. Added prestige was given to the event by having it in the Chapter House of Westminster Abbey. The paper says that Teilhard de Chardin was 'one of the greatest figures of our century' and 'has done more to reconcile science and theology than any other single scholar in the 20th century'. The main interest, however, is provided by the list of patrons of the exhibition who are — the Archbishop of Canterbury, the Archbishop of Westminster, the Moderator of the General Assembly of the Church of Scotland and the Dean of Westminster.

One cannot but help feeling that with such prestigious support as this, there would be little difficulty in sweeping to one side any critics who oppose Teilhard's fundamentally *un*Christian theology.]

That Teilhard was a member of (or received assistance from) one or more of the various organisations mentioned above I have no doubt. With the contacts that they can provide, he would have little difficulty in being a member of a small group intent on promoting the theory of evolution; a theory of great importance to him for upon it he was to later base all his philosophical writings.

I would suggest that it is by means of such clandestine organisations that the theory of evolution is given such prominence in the mass media whilst at the same time creationist evidence is deliberately barred. It is only by such censorship can the general public be sustained in their belief that they have developed from an ape ancestor when in truth they have been created in the image of God Himself.

If it were not for the fact that the end result is so disastrous for the human race, I would find it quite laughable to see so many intelligent men spending their lives arguing about minute features they have found on old bones that they claim link man with apes. I cannot but think that at times, in the quietness of their own hearts, they must surely have a deep sense of the fruitlessness and emptiness of their occupation when the link they are trying to establish so consistently refuses to close.

In my examination of many supposed ape-men fossils, it seems to me that the fraudulent nature of the claims made for them is so obvious that those who promote such evidence cannot but be aware of it also. If this is so, then their continued propagation of what they know to be a false theory cannot but result in them standing not just condemned, but self-condemned.

It should never be forgotten that on That Great Day, every single one of us will be held responsible for our every thought, word and deed.

There will be no excuses.

BIBLIOGRAPHY

1.   Spencer, F., 'Piltdown: A Scientific Forgery' Oxford Un. Press. 1990

2.   Spencer, F., 'The Piltdown Papers, 1908 - 1955: The Correspondence and other Documents Relating to the Piltdown Forgery.' Oxford Un. Press. 1990

3A. Vere, F., 'The Piltdown Fantasy' London 1955

3B 'Lessons of Piltdown' Evolution Protest Movement (Now Creation Science Movement) 1959.

4.   Weiner, J.S., 'The Piltdown Forgery' Oxford Un. Press 1955

5.   Bowden, M. 'Ape-men, Fact or Fallacy?' Second enlarged ed. 1981

6.   Costello, P., 'The Piltdown Hoax Reconsidered' Antiquity November 1985 vLIX p167-173.

7.   Costello, P., 'The Piltdown Hoax: Beyond the Hewitt Connection' Antiquity 1986 vLX p145-147

8.   Harrison, G.A., 'J.S. Weiner and the Exposure of the Piltdown Forgery' Antiquity March 1983 vLVII n219 p46-48.

APPENDIX 3 — KETTLEWELL'S EXPERIMENTS

In the course of correspondence with Prof. Sermonti, he sent me a copy of a paper he had written that would appear in Rivista di Biologia (later named Biology Forum), an Italian periodical published by Perugia University that he edited. The paper [1] was a critical examination of Kettlewell's experiments on the Peppered Moth — Biston betularia — and demonstrated that in a number of aspects the experiments were far from satisfactory or conclusive proof that the spread of the dark form of the moth was due to predation of the light form by birds.

I obtained Kettlewell's papers and fully agreed that they were far from conclusive, and were carried out in a way that could almost be considered as 'contrived', in order to produce the results that were expected. The following is a summary of some of the major inadequacies, and I would express my gratitude to Prof Sermonti for his very helpful paper that first brought the subject to the public's notice, upon which, together with a subsequent one [2], a number of the criticisms that follow are based.

In all the papers, the correct classified names were used for the three varieties that exist - typica (=normal, i.e.light), carbonaria (=dark) and insularia (intermediate speckled colouring that ranged from dark to light). In this appendix I will simply refer to the light and dark varieties, and generally omit references to the intermediate (insularia) variety, as the percentage of the latter was small. This variety was also excluded by Sermonti, and at times by Kettlewell in view of the low numbers.

Outline of the experiments

The experiments on the Peppered Moth were carried out by Kettlewell in the 1950's, there being 5 main ones —

1. The Barrel Experiment [3]. Light and dark moths were released into a barrel lined with black and white paper stripes. There were more moths on the the matching colour than on a contrasting colour to their own.

2. The Aviary experiment [4]. In this, moths were placed upon

light and dark trunks, and their capture by a pair of Great Tits was observed.

3. The first Birmingham Wood release experiment [4] carried out in a mainly oak wood that was blackened and free of lichen. Male moths of all three types were placed upon differing backgrounds in the early morning (as they fly and feed at night and shelter during the day). They were drawn to capture points the following night by Mercury Vapour Lamps or a captive young female. A higher percentage of dark ones were recaptured than light, indicating that the light ones had been taken by birds.

4. The Dorset wood experiment.[5] Here the trunks were unpolluted, and more light moths than dark were recaptured.

5. The second Birmingham wood experiment [5]. A repeat of the first one to check the results.

A resume of the main experiments appeared in the Proceeding of the Royal Society [6].

Kettlewell's detailed results of these experiments were set out in the various papers given in the reference section at the end of this appendix. There are a number of inadequacies and problematical results that could be highlighted and discussed, but a full examination of these many papers would be tedious. I will therefore deal with the major points under general headings.

1. THE INADEQUACIES OF THE EXPERIMENTS.

a) The positioning of the moths.

The moths were placed on the trunks in the dark early hours of the morning, having been specially bred for the experiments or held captive for many hours and days. Kettlewell notes that the moth 'was shaken from its box on to the bough or trunk. They generally wandered about for a few moments, and rapidly took up the optimum position available.' [4p333]. This suggests that the moths were dazed or sleepy from their experience. Some of them would have been used before, and had already undergone the trauma of captivity, release and recapturing with bright Mercury Vapour lights. The lights alone could have partially blinded them, making them less aware of their surroundings.

One major artificiality of the tests was that the moths were all placed on trees within reach of the ground for convenience of positioning them. They were therefore exposed to view to all predators. Kettlewell admits that this is unnatural and says —

'To the obvious criticism that the releases were not free to take up their own choice of resting site for the first day, I must answer that there were no other alternative backgrounds available for an insect that has to spend its days on trunks and boughs in this wood. I admit that, under their own choice, many would have taken up position higher in the trees, and that since the surface area of a tree increases proportional to the distance up the trunks or boughs, in so doing they would have avoided concentrations such as I produced ... Others have shown the importance to cryptic [camouflaged] insects of avoiding too high a density, but this is no argument against the findings for the *relative* advantages of the three forms. It must be accepted, however, that, under natural conditions, predation, though selective, might take place at a lower tempo.' [4p340]

Kettlewell is here glossing over what is really a very important point. The further apart the moths are placed, the less likelihood of them being taken by birds. This was confirmed in both the aviary and the Birmingham experiments. In the aviary, the moths were visible but untouched for two hours, as the Tits had not seen them. Then in the next hour they had all been eaten. Similarly in Birmingham, when a bird discovered a moth, (usually a light one) it searched the area closely for others, and soon all the nearby moths had been taken, including many dark ones.

But the aspect of density of the moths resting places is not the only factor that affects their predation. One worker [2p14] provided evidence that the moths, far from resting on trunks of trees, as Kettlewell had artificially placed them, actually rested on the underside of small horizontal branches high up in the canopy. Being higher in the trees, they would have been far more widely dispersed and well screened from view by the foliage, thus reducing the importance of their different colouration even further and making detection far more difficult.

Kettlewell did no specific experiments in which the moths were allowed to find their own resting place during the day, but in the first Birmingham experiment 29 moths were captured after 48 hours freedom which means that they had one day when they were able to select their own resting place. The results were dark - 25 - 5.72% of releases, intermediate - 2 - 4.35%, light - 2 - 1.48%. These returns are so small a percentage of the total released that no significance can be placed upon them. It is also strange that the percentage of intermediates returning was almost as high as the dark form, which would indicate that their speckled colouring was not as disadvantageous as might be thought.

That the moths would have taken up a more concealed position in nature than the visible ones forced upon them by Kettlewell is indicated in the aviary experiments. Here Kettlewell mentions that some experiments had to be abandoned ' ... when pouring rain caused movement on the part of the insects ... ' [4p330] This tends to confirm that they rested beneath high level branches that they would have naturally sought in nature, which would have sheltered them from rain. When they experienced it in the aviary, they tried to move elsewhere.

Density and predation.

Examining the subject of the density of the moths on the trees further, Sermonti notes that the first few releases in Birmingham were low density and resulted in a very low percentage return on the following night (the count was taken in the early hours of the next day).

It must be remembered that Kettlewell was well aware of the importance and distorting effect that high density of positioning the moths on the trees could have for he refers to the works of others who had already highlighted this factor. He also knew from he aviary experiment that once the birds had seen one of the moths, they eagerly searched the boughs nearby for more and took both the light and dark forms. He notes ' ... they were quick to learn and took freely both light and dark forms of betularia' [4p330].

Similarly, from observations of the first releases he notes 'From this it would appear that when a conspicuous insect had been found, it at once put other insects in the immediate vicinity at a disadvantage because of the birds active searchings.' [4p336].

In the first three releases 154 moths were positioned on 33 trees, averaging 1.5 moths per tree, but over the following 5 nights only 22 (14%) were recaptured (12 dark, 5 light, 5 intermediate). This was too small a return to provide any significant results. Without any comment or explanation we find that in the following 5 releases he used a total of 476 moths. Assuming that they were still being positioned on the 33 trees available, this gives a density per release of 2.9 moths per tree. The recaptures were much higher at 127 (111 dark, 13 light, 3 intermediate).

These levels of density of positioning of moths is several orders higher than that estimated by some workers, which is given as 7-22 moths /km2/night [2p14] — an extremely low value. Kettlewell's densities are so much higher and the moths are in such highly visible locations that these experiments are quite artificial, and cannot in any way be looked upon as having any relevance to the natural situation.

The Dorset experiment started with a high density release (84 on

20 trees), and again he reported that this resulted in many of the moths being taken by the birds, both light and dark. He therefore discounted this result and in the next release used 27 on 23 trees.

Now with the density of release being established as an important factor, one might have expected this value to be obtainable from the data he gives. In fact, however, no figures on this aspect are presented, and the subject becomes extremely vague.

In the first release he mentions 'These [84] were released on only twenty trees, the reason for this small number being that I had been unable to locate and prepare the other trees in the area'. Quite what 'preparation' was required he does not say. It may have been to mark the trees with a number, but then might this not have drawn the attention of the birds to them? We are not told.

In the second release the following day, there are still only 23 trees available on which he places 27 moths. However, in subsequent releases, on 10 days he used a total of 777 moths (roughly equal numbers of light and dark), the highest number being 125 on one day. How many trees he used he does not record but he does make the following interesting comment.

'All other releases were in fact conducted in a uniform manner ... In these, on every occasion, there was one phenotype released per tree, and the experiment was conducted over a larger area of woodland ... One further point was noted, that the same trees must not be used as release points on each day, as the birds became conditioned to them.' [5p298]

Regarding the number of trees, he says that a larger area of woodland was used, which suggests more trees were available, but on the other hand, they could not be used on every release. Thus it is possible that only some 20-25 trees may have been available for any one release. This would have made the density still very high indeed, which is one of the features he stresses he was at pains to avoid. As already noted however, we are not given the facts.

It is the second sentence however that is the more intriguing. In the initial reading of it, one might assume that only one moth was used on each tree, but this is not necessarily so, for he simply says 'phenotype'. Thus it could be interpreted to say that he may have put more than one moth on a tree but they were all of the same type. This would have had a very profound consequence, for it was by now well established that putting light and dark on the same (light) tree resulted in not only the dark ones being eaten, but many of the light ones also. The dark ones initially attracted the bird to the tree whereupon it found many others nearby of the light variety.

If, as he seems to be saying, he put several of the same colour on each tree, the result would have been that almost certainly the many dark ones would have been taken quickly, whilst the light ones would have been less likely to have been seen. The result would have been a high mortality of the dark ones and a much higher survival of the light variety, the ratio being greatly exagerrated due to the positioning of the moths in the first place.

One could go even further. We have no means of knowing from the paucity of information how dense the moths were on the trees, and there arises the possiblity that the light ones were sparsely distributed on the trees with perhaps only one or two per tree, whilst the dark moths were placed with a much higher density, almost ensuring their capture. I would not of course suggest that he would have made such an error, but it is indeed unfortunate that he did not provide the information that would have dispelled any such suspicion.

In nature, the density of 7-22 moths/km2/night is extremely low, and as a result, the possiblity of a bird seeing even a contrasting moth would have been very infrequent. There is even less likelihood of its capture subsequently leading to the predation of a nearby camouflaged moth — as occured in Kettlewell's experiments on a number of occasions. Thus the part that predation played in the increase in the number of the dark variety is almost negligible — as other writers had already claimed. We will see later, however, that calculations would be made on the results of these experiments, but as the conditions were so artificial, the mathematical results are virtually worthless.

b) The camouflage of the moths.

Kettlewell carried out some experiments [3] to see if the moths deliberately chose a background that matched their colouring by releasing moths into a cider barrel covered with stripes of black and white paper. A total of 198 moths were released into the barrel, 99 each of light and dark. Of these, 88 were half way between stripes and were discounted from the results, 77 chose a matching background and 41 a contrasting colour. In considering these results Kettlewell claims 'It would appear, therefore that the black and pale forms appreciate their immediate backgrounds.', and this conclusion is repeated in many of his reports.

Is such a conclusion fully justifiable however? Of the total released, 39% were found on their matching background, which Kettlewell claims is a sufficient number to prove his point. But looked at from the opposite end, 61% were so uncaring which background they chose that they sat either across two stripes, or even on the wrong ones. Such behaviour, which Kettlewell would claim is a matter of life or death to each moth, seems to be of little concern to the moths themselves!

Kettlewell in fact quotes [4p340] a study by another expert who watched the positioning of another light and dark form of moth on three types of wall. The conclusion was that ' ... the effect of natural selection is quite negligible as a factor in progressive melanism.' Now this was a carefully observed experiment in nature that was carried out over a long period of time and which gave a clear result. Despite this, Kettlewell virtually brushes this evidence to one side and presents arguments why such a conclusion can be ignored, claiming that

> 'Consequently there is, theoretically, no limit set to the smallness of an advantage which can be used in selection, and one involving one out of 300 individuals indicates quite a considerable selective influence (Fisher 1930). Fortunately, in the present series of experiments the values are of a much higher order and the effects of natural selection on industrial melanics for crypsis [camouflage] in such areas can no longer be disputed.'

In this claim, it should be noted that he refers to the work of Fisher, the value of whose theories we have already commented upon in section II A 4 — 'Mathematical theories'. It has already been pointed out above that Kettlewell admits that in nature, where the moths would be higher in the trees, the predation rate he recorded would be lower by a value he does not care to even guess at. Yet here he contends that the high rate of predation that he obtained confirms the fact that it is a major factor in producing a large proportion of blackened forms of moths.

One other factor little realised is that Kettlewell chose the Birmingham site very carefully, and used an oak wood that had also 10% of birch, and which was isolated on three sides by fields and gardens. It was however part of a larger wood which 'had sundry other copses almost exclusively consisting of birch.' [4p330]

Thus the part of the wood he chose was heavily biassed against the light form, but not far away were large parts of the wood which favoured the light moths. Therefore, looking at the whole woodland around, there were plenty of areas that favoured the survival of the light form, yet they were well outnumbered by the dark ones. This indicates that the reason for the predominance of the dark form was not predation of the light, but some other mechanism.

Kettlewell chose the particularly dark oak section of the wood to assist in obtaining the results from predation that he was seeking. Had he carried out a second experiment in one of the lighter birch copses, on his theory he would have got a quite different result i.e., a higher survival of the light variety. But this would not have suited

his ideas, for the dark form were presumably predominant in both
the oak and the birch areas. He therefore, as we know, went down
to Dorset to make the reverse experiment, where the result would
have 'agreed' with the predominance of the light form he knew
prevailed there.

c) The failure of the Dorset check experiment.

In order to check if the Mercury Vapour lamps and females
recapture system attracted one type more then the other, (i.e., they
were giving biased results) Kettlewell released 22 dark and 40 light
moths between 5 and 6 p.m. — when they would not have been
subjected to predation by the birds. With this number released, the
return to the traps that night was expected to be about 21% of those
released, i.e. 4-5 dark and 8-9 light. In fact he caught 7 dark and 6
light (32% and 15%). To trap twice as large a proportion of dark than
light was completely unexpected and Kettlewell tried to explain this
fact away. He simply said that clearly the traps did not favour the
lights more than the dark moths, but this does not provide any
explanation at all of why the test caught far more dark moths than
it should have done.

Kettlewell made no attempt to use this check release in his
conclusions, which he should have done. Instead, he declared that
the result is eliminated from the summary values in assessing the
results of the whole Dorset experiment. The test was to check any
tendency for the traps to capture one type against the other, and the
most obvious answer was that it did in fact attract more dark than
light ones. In view of this, he should surely have used the results to
correct all the other results in some way — such as multiplying the
recaptures by a factor derived from this test. This he did not do, as
such a correction would have grossly distorted the results that he had
already obtained.

Indeed, if we stop and think about the experiments at the two
sites in the light of this unexpected result we can come to vastly
different conclusions to those which Kettlewell was wanting to
draw. In the light Dorset wood he expected to collect a low number
of dark moths after the birds had been feeding, and this broadly
speaking was what he obtained. The test without predation however
showed that a large proportion of dark moths were attracted to the
traps, which really puts a question mark over all the tests in this
wood.

In the dark Birmingham wood, he obtained more dark moths
after predation, again as expected. Considering this result in the
light of the Dorset test, however, it could obviously be insisted that
the dark moths were more attracted to the traps than the light variety,

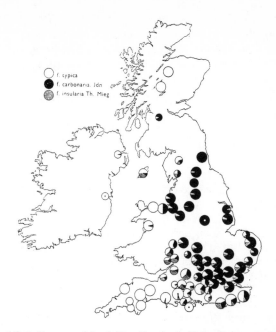

Fig. A3.1 Geographical distribution of the Peppered Moth

and it was for *this* reason that he obtained the results that he did, and *not* due to predation as he claimed it was. Thus the Dorset test result completely negates all the experiments carried out in Birmingham!

In trying to explain away this unexpected result, he appealed to the satisfactory balance of trapping that he had obtained in the first Birmingham experiment and other peripheral reasons, but he is clearly troubled by this result and does not give any satisfactory explanation.

After he had completed the work in Dorset he then went direct to Birmingham for the second set of tests. He could have there carried out a similar recapture test without predation as he had in Dorset, but this was not done. Did he perhaps not wish to obtain yet another result that would have upset the neat conclusion of selective predation that he was trying to demonstrate with the whole series of laborious experiments that he was undertaking?

2. GEOGRAPHICAL DISTRIBUTION

It is here that another serious objection to Kettlewell's conclusions can be made. The first investigation into the 'problem of industrial melanism' was in 1900.

A few figures for collections of varieties of moths were published, but no strong conclusions could be drawn from them. Kettlewell therefore contacted over 150 collectors of insects to gather information about the frequency and distribution of the three types of Peppered Moths. He obtained a large number of results, which he set out in reference 6. He grouped the numbers into 83 centres and gave the results in a pictorial form which is shown in Figure A1.1

It will be seen that the dark variety prevail to the west of a line drawn down the industrial centre of the nation. Kettlewell says this map shows:

'a) A correlation between the frequency of the melanic [dark and intermediate] forms and the industrial areas of Britain.
'b) A high frequency of carbonaria [dark variety] throughout eastern England from north to south, though far removed from industrial centres. This is, in my opinion, the indirect effect of long continued smoke fall-out carried by the prevailing south-westerly winds from central England.' [7p58]

He admits that there are several other factors that could have affected the colouration of the moths but does not dwell on them in any detail, but emphasises the predation of the birds of the light variety. Certainly his broad conclusions appear reasonable, but a careful consideration of the map shows some anomalies.

Firstly, although there is a general drift of the dark variety to the north east of the industrial centre around Birmingham, it is hardly likely that the pollution is so very extensive as far away as the Norfolk coast, that it could explain the 67 and 77 % of the dark form surviving.

Secondly, there is a fairly high percentage (46) of dark moths recorded at Folkstone, and for this to have been due to a soot laden atmosphere borne by the prevailing south-westerly wind would have required an industrial centre somewhere in the English Channel! In a similar way, the high 89% of dark forms recorded for Bromley could not be due to any polluted industrial atmosphere, as I can vouch for both present and in the past.

Migration — the real cause?

Kettlewell carried out some tests of just how far a Peppered Moth usually travelled over a period of time. He came to the conclusion that the moth 'frequently flies a mile per night, probably much further.'[7p60]. That migration on this scale was one of the principle reasons for the spread of the dark moth he rejects in the very next sentence saying 'Nevertheless, dispersal cannot be accepted as the actual cause of f. carbonaria [dark form]'. He gives no reasons whatsoever for this rejection, but follows this statement by referring to 'considerable evidence that recurrent mutation, at a fairly high rate also takes place', and refers to sites where the dark form had been found or established itself independaently of any others, from whom they were separated by great distance or natural barriers.

But a high rate of mutation that produced the dark form has nothing to do with predation. Indeed, he mentions that a high percentage of the dark variety had established itself in Stroud in Gloucestershire and Maidstone in Kent — areas hardly likely to be seriously blackened by industrial pollution.

Jone's article in 'nature.'

A short but very interesting article was written by J S Jones and appeared in Nature [8]. In this he made a number of points which I summarise below.

a) Darkening of species also occured in industrial Britain amongst beetles, cats and birds which are not subject to predation. In Ladybirds the darkening gave them increased efficiency in absorbtion of sunlight in smokey atmospheres. In pigeons, the darkening was due to hormonal changes allowing year-round breeding due to year-round availability of food.

b) Dark forms of other moths were common in forests long

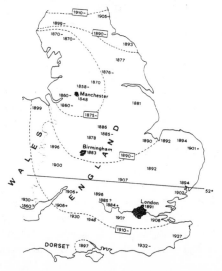

Fig. A3.2 Migration of the dark form.

before the Industrial Revolution. In the newly polluted cities of America they expanded rapidly as the variants spread *from* the forests.

c) The dark form never rose above 95% even in the most polluted areas, yet tests had shown that it should have replaced the lighter form if it was solely due to predation.

d) The dark form reaches 80% in rural East Anglia where there is little industrial pollution, which cannot be explained by predation.

e) He refers to a computer model by Mani that divides the whole of the country up into squares and allows it to run for 150 generations — from the beginning of the Industrial Revolution to the present day — and found that with certain inputs (e.g. the approximate rate of migration as 2.5 Km per generation), it closely resembled the present day distribution of the ratios between the light and dark forms in the various areas.

Jones finishes his article with the following passage.

'The best fit of Mani's predicted frequencies to those found in nature is obtained using estimates of *non-visual selection* [emphasis mine] which differ slightly from those resulting from breeding experiments. Nevertheless, his results make it clear that the evolution of industrial melanism in B. betularia must depend in part on gene flow and on powerful *non-visual selective forces whose nature is as yet unknown* [emphasis mine]. There remain many other problems associated with this apparently straightforward example of natural selection. Why, for example has the frequency of carbonaria decreased in northern England since the introduction of smoke control, but increased in the south? Even for a melanic moth it seems that life is never as simple as made out in the text books.' [8]

It becomes increasingly likely that the real cause of the spread of the dark variety was mainly by migration, despite Kettlewell's denial. Sermonti in fact reproduces a map from another writer which I have shown as Figure A1/2. From this it can be seen that the most likely centre from which the migration started was north of Manchester, and the dark form spread across the country into both polluted and unpolluted areas.

As we have already considered, the freedom that the moths would have had in nature to disperse themselves high in the foliage of any available tree during the daytime would have greatly reduced the possiblity of their being captured, and therefore the difference in predation due to the variety of their coloration would have been negligible.

... or feeding habits?

One of the surprising conclusions reached by Lambert et al [2] is that an important factor in the darkening of the moths is their environment, and particularly their feeding habits. They refer to the very carefully conducted experiments carried out between 1919 and 1957 by J.W. Heslop Harrison (amongst others), who fed moths on industrially polluted vegetation and obtained a dark form in a number of the offspring. This seems to give support to the Lamarkian theory of the inheritance of acquired characteristics in a limited form. In this article, there are several interesting claims and I give a brief outline of some of them.

i) After feeding several generations of a moth on polluted plants, one black female appeared which when mated with a white male produced 21 all black offspring. This suggests that the black form could spread rapidly in any area.

ii) Kettlewell obtained dark moths from pupae that had been heated.

iii) The results of Harrison's work were commented on by the mathematician Fisher, but his view are dismissed by Lambert who says 'It should be pointed out that these are not criticisms of Harrison's experiments but rather they represent an attempt to fit them to the then-current notions about mutations'

iv) The inheritance of the darker features was held to be due to ' ... a dynamic interplay between genetic elements within the nucleus and those in the cytoplasm [the general material within the cell]' [9p28]. This is indeed a profound and surprising contention, but not out of line with the whole subject of cortical inheritance which we have examined above. Indeed, the authors quote one worker who says

> 'The cell is an intergrated system in which every genetic unit influences the other.' [2p28]

Thus, from this approach, the genetic material is not just in the genes of the nucleus as most people accept, nor is it in the cortex in addition, as we have suggested in the section on the topic, but the whole cell may have an influence on the final outcome of the fusion of the two germ cells.

The whole subject is fairly technical, and the interested reader is referred to this paper for further information and references to this important aspect of genetics and seeming inheritance of features that may be the result of the environment. With all this, however, these experiments have only produced a darkening of a moths coloration.

Whether the darkening was due to migration or genetic changes or a combination of both is for further study, but what is clear is that predation played virtually no part in it. No new species has arisen, only a variety of an existing one. The popular presentation of Kettlewell's contrived experiments as proof of the evolution of a new species is surely little less than deception of the public that has been successful for far too long.

Haldane's mathematics

Immediately following Kettlewell's summary paper in the Proceedings of the Royal Society [6] were two papers by Haldane on the mathematical calculations of the survival value of the dark form [9]. As noted before, the formulae are incomprehensible to the non-specialist, but some of his comments are of interest. The numerous assumptions that he has to make in formulating his figures are clear on the first page. As we have noted, Kettlewell had admitted that in nature the predation rate would be much lower than the values he obtained. Even though he seems to ignore this unquantifiable factor in his calculations, Haldane has to admit —

> 'I conclude, either that selection is much less intense than Kettlewell found, that immigration from unpolluted areas is important (which is unlikely) or that selection has slowed down for a reason that I consider.' [9p304]

Having provided a dazzling display of mathematics he nevertheless seems to accept that the results are inconclusive for he ends his first paper with the weak admission

> ' ... that numerical calculations of the type here given are of a certain value if only as suggesting further experiments

Macbeth's scathing remarks given in section A4 on mathematical theories in genetics still appear to be warranted.

The evolutionary presuppositions

In the reading of Kettlewell's papers, it gradually becomes clear that he was a convinced believer in the theory of evolution, and the whole of his experiments were carried out to the end of adding further proof of its correctness. There are suggestions in some of his comments that he knew the sort of results that he was looking for. Examples of such references are —

'The industrial melanism the Lepidoptera is the most striking evolutionary change ever actually witnessed in any organism, animal or plant.' [4p323]

He repeats this statement in his Summary in Ref.4 as item No.1 [p341], and continues to say in subsequent items;

'Item 2. In order to account for its success, a theory has been assumed in which an inter-relation exists between the superior visibility of certain melanics and predation by birds which eliminate resting moths selectively.'
Item 4. In general, predation by birds has been thought to be responsible for the evolution of concealing colour patterns in moths.
Item 5. In spite of exhaustive observations, however, no evidence of such a selective elimination has, up to now, ever been produced. This paper supplies it. [Comment - despite several experiments which Kettlewell classes as 'exhausting', they nevertheless failed to provide the badly needed proof. Could it not be that it is Kettlewell's experiments that contradict them that are in error?]
Item 14 ... Consequently birds act as selective agents, as postulated by evolutionary theory.'

At the start of his article in The Scientific American [10] Kettlewell begins by paying a lengthy homage to Darwin and his ' ... 26 years of laborious accumulation of facts ... ' but notes that he had no knowledge of the mechanism of heredity, and ' ... no visible example of evolution at work in nature.' He continues by regretting that Mendel's laws of inheritance ' ... were not discovered by the community of biologists until 1900 ... ', but then claims that the most striking evolutionary change 'was taking place around him [Darwin] in his own country' [i.e. industrial melanism]

He claimed that the replacement of the light by the dark form of moth " ... indicates that this evolutionary mechanism is remarkably flexible." and that 'Industrial melanism involves no new laws of nature; it is governed by the same mechanisms which have brought about the evolution of new species in the past.'

He concludes the article by saying 'Had Darwin observed industrial melanism ... he would have witnessed the consummation and confirmation of his life's work'"[10p53]. Sermonti wryly comments after reviewing Kettlewell's experiments 'The evidence Darwin lacked, Kettlewell lacked as well.'

The Royal Society.

In the section above headed 'Geographical Distribution', reference is made to the first serious investigation into the ' ... problem of industrial melanism ... ' in 1900.

What is of particular interest is that this is a reference to the consideration of the subject in 1900 by the Evolution Committee of no less a body than the Royal Society. Clearly, the possibility that the darkening of these moths was due to a process of 'natural selection' that could be used in support of evolution had been noted by this committee many years before Kettlewell's experiments, and papers had already appeared on the subject before Kettlewell's.

That the Royal Society actually established a committee devoted to the propagation of evolution is intriguing. That the Society, in the interest of subjective balance and fairmindedness might also have formed a Creation Committee is to be doubted!

[I will digress at this point to note that I have already described elsewhere [11p112f] the considerable influence that this body, under the control of the powerful 'X Club', had upon the imposition of the theory of evolution upon the rapidly expanding academic society of the nation.]

It is an oft made excuse that evolution acts so slowly that you cannot see significant changes even over many years. Nevertheless, clearly there had been a desire for several years to obtain some evidence of evolution within a short period of time, and industrial melanism in moths looked to be one of the most likely examples. The numerous experiments were quite costly in both time and materials. For example at the Devon site at Dene End Wood, sheds had to be found to house the three thousand betularia pupae. The whole of this experiment and the second Birmingham experiment was funded by the Nuffield Foundation.

When Kettlewell published the results of his 'successful' experiments, the news was circulated world wide. They are quoted as the 'classic example' of evolution occuring within a short period of time. I would nevertheless contend that they contain many inadequacies which render them inconclusive, and that predation is comparatively irrelevant as an explanation of the increase of the dark form of the moth. However, as it was the only evidence available that could show 'evolution in action', its shortcomings were carefully glossed over. It duly entered the very fertile area of school textbooks in a very short space of time, where it continues to do its work as propaganda for the theory of evolution to this day.

REFERENCES TO APPENDIX 3

1   Sermonti G and Catastini P,   1984 'On Industrial Melanism — Kettlewell's missing evidence' Rivista di Biologia 77 No 1 p35 - 52.

2 Lambert, D.M., Millar, C.D., and Hughes, T.J. 'On the Classic Case of Natural Selection' Rivista di Biologia — Biology Forum v79 v1 p11-29 and 45-49. March 1986

3   Kettlewell H B D., 1955 28th May 'Recognition of the appropriate backgrounds by the pale and black phases of Lepidoptera'. Nature v175 p943-944

4 Kettlewell H B D, 1955 'Selection experiments on industrial melanism in the Lepidoptera' Heredity (London) v9 p323-342

5   Kettlewell H B D, 1956 December 'Further selection experiments on industrial melanism in the Lepidoptera'. Heredity v10 part 3 p287-301

6 Kettlewell H B D, 1956 'A resume of investigations on the evolution of melanism in the Lepidoptera'. Proc. Royal Society v145B p297-306

7 Kettlewell H B D, 1958 'A survey of the frequencies of Biston Betularia (L) (Lep.) and its melanic forms in Great Britain' Heredity (London) v12 p51-72

8 Jones J. S., 1982 11 November 'More to melanism than meets the eye' Nature v300 p109-110

9 Haldane, J. 'The Theory of Selection for Melanism in Lepidoptera' Proc. Royal Society v145B p303-306 1956

10   Kettlewell H B D, 1959 'Darwin's missing evidence' Scientific American. v200 part 3 p48-53

11 Bowden, M., 'The Rise of the Evolution Fraud' Sovereign Publications 1982

APPENDIX 4 — A LIST OF DECEPTIVE STRATAGEMS

When searching for the stratagems that writers and speakers might adopt, I was a little surprised to find that no full list of them was given in any of the reference works that were immediately available. The following list is therefore as complete as I could put together of the various stratagems that any writer might use in discussing any subject. It may therefore be of use as a reference when examining a wide range of topics apart from evolution. In what follows I will simply give the main methods with illustrations, and then leave it to the reader to examine books by evolutionists to spot which particular stratagem is being used. Often more than one method will be used at any one time in order to persuade the reader to agree with the author's viewpoint.

....

1) VAGUE PHRASEOLOGY

A general phrase is used to gloss over a weakness in the evidence in order not to arouse the suspicions of the reader.

I have already given one example where the theory of recapitulation was clearly known to be discredited. Nevertheless, the writer was so keen to use the 'evidence' that this was virtually ignored in the text following the diagram of the embryos. Another from the same popular book is not dissimilar.

In the section on 'Immunology', I mentioned that I would be considering one phrase that the writer used in referring to the results of blood serum precipitates in attempting to find the relationships between many different species. The particular sentence is 'Immunological evidence is not direct proof of evolutionary relationship, but contributes to the weight of evidence for that view' [37p28]

If one considers for a moment the implication behind the phrase ' ... not direct proof ... ' it should be asked, 'Why is it not direct proof?' It is admitted that there are forms of evidence that are more circumstantial than hard factual proof, and where a case is proven by a quite different sets of facts, these can be referred to in general support of a case, although not themselves conclusive.

This however is not the situation regarding these scientific experiments on blood serum, several thousand of which were carried out. There was thus ample data available for analysis and for the forming of an opinion. The results themselves, however, were far from conclusive evidence in support of evolution. As I have mentioned, there was naturally a general trend that 'near relations' (on the evolutionary scale .i.e. 'more advanced') organisms gave more precipitate than 'distant' ('simpler') species, and the writer uses this as justification for claiming that the evidence supported evolution and included a section on immunology in her book. That the relationships are fallacious is glossed over by the phrase ' ... not direct proof ... '

Other phrases in books on evolution hide the real truth behind them. Some examples are as follows;

'This constancy..despite differences in detail ... '. This can hide the fact that the differences seriously undermine the theory. However, as the majority of results support evolution, they are therefore emphasised and the contradictory evidence is glossed over.

'There is evidence that ... ' This could mean that out of a mass of evidence, certain items will be emphasised, and contradictory evidence ignored.

Phrases such as ' ... possibly ... ', ' ... probably ... ', ' ... almost certainly ... ' and many other such guarded satements should alert the reader to the fact that the writer does not really have convincing proof for his following statement. These phrases are used in all scientific works where some degree of supposition is acceptable, but the frequency with which they occur in books about evolution is far greater than in most other subjects.

2) FALSE ANALOGIES.

In order to explain a point an analogy is used (usually beginning with the words — 'It is like ... ') but the picture presented is not applicable to the situation being considered. It is essential that the generalisation that the analogy is used to illustrate should accurately reflect the particular aspect of the subject that the writer wants to illustrate. It must stand up to logical analysis and comparison between the two situations. This is one of the most deceptive methods that is used.

In one TV programme dealing with the gaps in the fossil record, the speaker claimed that there could be a build-up of genetic codes for a new development in a species, and that when the situation was suitable, they would suddenly all be activated in complete harmony to produce a new feature, such as a new organ the animal could use. In order to illustrate this sudden emergence, he produced the child's toy that consists of a small piece of curved spring in a holder, which when pressed buckles into a new position with a loud click. When released it springs back with another click.

Clicking this toy to the new position was to demonstrate how simple it was for new genes to spring into action when they could be effective, and the loud noise no doubt helped to fix the idea in the minds of many viewers.

However, this analogy is unacceptable. The spring is a simple piece of metal that is curved to be stable in only two positions, and the changeover is sufficiently sudden to produce a sharp noise. In contrast, the genetic changes that have to be made are complex in the extreme, and all have to be carefully co-ordinated in precise detail if they are to be fully effective when operating. There is no known mechanism that could bring this about, so the use of such an analogy is completely misleading.

3) ASSUMPTIONS BECOME EVIDENCE.

What is assumed in one chapter, is referred to as 'a fact' in a later chapter.

This is the thinking behind such phrases as 'It is probable (likely / possible) that … ' where the evidence is thin, but the writer seeks to draw the conclusions that he needs.

Darwin in his lengthy 'Origin of Species' discussed various problems facing his theory, often finishing with a phrase such as 'It is therefore possible that … '. In a later chapter he would say 'As we have shown … ', and what was an assumption is taken as proven fact.

I have noted in the section on 'limits to breeding' the way in which he glossed over the inability of breeders to obtain new species, claiming that it was 'rash to assert … ' that a limit could be placed on the effects of breeding.' The whole of his book however is based on the assumption that new species *have* emerged, and Darwin tries to provide a mechanism for the process.

4) STRAW MEN.

This is to give a grossly inadequate description of a viewpoint (or the views of an individual) which is then criticised for its weaknesses. The weaknesses however are really of the critic's own making. When an able expert is given an opportunity to reply, the falseness of the picture they have painted usually become very obvious.

An example is the statement in the handbook of the British Natural History Museum entitled 'Origin of Species' [12]. This reads —

'Why are there so many different kinds of living things? One view is that all living things were created just as we see them today, *and have never changed.* Another view is that the living things we see today have all *evolved* [emphasis theirs] from some distant ancestor by a process of gradual change.' [12p7]

As the rest of the book then describes just how much change has taken place in animals, both natural and by breeding, the obvious inference is that as they could not have been created as fixed species, they therefore must have evolved.

But creationists do *not* say that animals have never changed. What we do say is that such changes are only varieties of the same species, that these varieties can only range between certain limits, and that it is impossible to proceed from one species to a completely different one with a series of large or small links between them.

Thus the creationist case is misrepresented in order to discredit it.

[Whilst examining this book, I noticed that in their short booklist at the back they recommended Patterson's 'Evolution'. This was also published by the Museum but as we have seen, it is not as fully supportive of the theory as they might have wished. They also mentioned Macbeth's highly critical book 'Darwin Retried'. Their note however simply says 'A lawyer's view of the evidence for natural selection'. From this it could be inferred that he had examined it and pronounced it well substantiated from a legal point of view. There is no indication that his book is actually a scathing indictment of the whole theory of evolution.]

5) FILTERING THE EVIDENCE.

From the vast amount of evidence available, most of which contradicts the theory, the small amount of evidence that seems to support evolution is greatly emphasised, and the much stronger contra-evidence is either ignored or misconstrued.

I have in another work [26p131] described the preparation for the BBC radio programme in 1981 in which several creationists were interviewed for quite a long time with a tape recorder running by the individual interviewers. In the final broadcast, all the strong claims of the evidence against the theory were edited out, and only the most innocuous phrases that did little to promote the creationist veiwpoint were presented.

This is in fact the most frequently used tactic of the evolutionists.

Indeed, books about evolution can only be written by ignoring the great weight of evidence against it.

6) 'AD HOC' THEORIES.

When faced with contradictory facts, in order to maintain the integrity of the main theory, an explanation is provided, usually with little or no supporting evidence. That a seemingly reasonable explanation exists is often held to be sufficient for accepting that this was in fact what happened.

Every time a comet passes around the sun, a considerable quantity of its frozen material is burnt off by the heat of the sun, and it is this which forms the 'tail' of the comet. A number of comets have fairly short return periods of only a few hundred years — Halley's comet being one of the shortest at 76 years. It has been calculated that these comets should have been completely burnt away within a period of about 10,000 years, which is very much less than the 4,500 million years that is claimed to be the age of the earth. Unable to accept the direct evidence that the earth was only a few thousand years old, the evolutionists had to account for their existence today. This problem was overcome by Oort, who suggested that there was a 'cloud' of comets circling around in outer space, that were disturbed by a passing star and thus began their journey towards the solar system.

There is no evidence whatsoever that such a cloud of comets exists and this theory was invented simply to overcome the age problem that the existence of short term comets presented to evolutionists.

7) BEGGING THE QUESTION (CIRCULAR REASONING).

The line of the argument is twisted back so that what was to be proved is taken as proven.

I have already described the circular reasoning involved with the way in which the fossils date the strata, and the strata are then subsequently dated by the fossils.

In an earlier book of the British Natural History Museum entitled 'Evolution' [88] de Beer says that he will prove that 'those who invoke mathematical improbability can be refuted out of their own mouths.' He quotes the work of Muller who calculated that the chance of getting from an amoeba to a horse by means of mutations is one thousand raised to the power of one million. de Beer then triumphantly proclaims;

> 'This impossible and meaningless figure serves to illustrate the power of natural selection in collecting favourable mutations and minimising waste of variations, for horses *do* [emphasis his] exist and they *have* [emphasis his] evolved.' [77p19]

I will pass by the fact that the vast numbers of mutations still have to take place for natural selection can only select from features that have developed. Examining the line of argument shows that de Beer dismisses perfectly reasonable mathematical calculations that show that horses could not have evolved by mutations. He simply says that as horses nevetheless exist, the mathematics are therefore wrong, and consequently they *must* have evolved. The extremely poor logic behind this statement is surely obvious.

8) 'A PRIORI' (DEDUCTIVE) REASONING.

A fact is deduced from something beforehand, as when we infer certain effects from given causes. Mathematical proofs are of this kind.

For example, evolutionists would claim that the Law of Natural Selection ensures that the faster animals are able to escape their predators, and thus live to have strong offspring. Natural selection is considered to be the cause of fast healthy animals surviving, but there could be other factors apart from this Law that have not been considered.

9) 'A POSTERIORI' (INDUCTIVE) REASONING.

The deduction of the cause from observing the act. This is the opposite of 'a priori' reasoning, and is the form of judgement used in the Law Courts.

The best example of this is Paley's argument that if we find a watch, then we may rightly deduce that there was a watchmaker. The observation of an object or incident leads us to the conclusion that there was a preceding cause or intention that resulted in the facts that are witnessed.

Evolutionists would of course claim that their whole theory is based upon a large number of observed facts that Darwin first set out in a scientific form.

10) 'POST HOC ERGO PROPTER HOC' (After this, therefore because of this).

Because a certain action was taken. which was followed by a subsequent incident, the first is incorrectly assumed to have caused the second.

This is best illustrated by Mark Twain's comment 'I joined the Confederacy for two weeks. Then I deserted. The Confederacy fell.'

As an example, an explanation that has been put forward for the disappearance of dinosaurs at the end of the Cretaceous period is as follows.

There is a layer between the Cretaceous and the Paleocene strata above it that contains two rare metals. These metals are also found in asteroids and meteorites. Dinosaurs died out at the end of the Cretaceous. Therefore the impact of a meteorite was the cause of the world wide extinction of dinosaurs.

This is only one of very many explanations that have been proposed to explain the sudden disappearance of dinosaurs in the fossil record, but the leap in the line of reasoning of this explanation is clear.

11) EQUIVOCATION.

Changing the meaning of a word in the course of the discussion.

The word 'Law' can sometimes be misapplied. A discussion of the the universal and unavoidable Law of Gravity may be subtly led on to referring to the Law of Natural Selection, giving it the same status of inevitability as that of gravity. But some weak and unfit animals *do* survive and have offspring, thus contradicting the concept of it being a 'Law' that is unchangeable.

12) FALLACIOUS APPEAL TO AUTHORITY.

A well known name in one subject is used as a voice of authority in an area in which he is not an expert.

Thus it might be claimed that a great political leader of the nation fully accepts the theory of evolution, with the implication that the listener should be impressed with the prestigious support the theory has, and therefore should not criticise it from his little knowledge.

This question of authority is an important one, and is sometimes used in the reverse way. For example, an approach may be made to some national body such as the BBC, pointing out a number of facts that are against evolution, and that their publicity for the theory is misguided. The reply that has been received is that they 'have consulted the very best authorities and all agree that the theory is well substantiated.' Thus prestigious authorities are appealed to as decisive, irrespective of the correctness or otherwise of the evidence presented.

13) PERSONALISED ABSTRACTIONS.

Such phrases as 'Science proves that ... ', 'History teaches us ... ' ignore the fact that actually many different interpretations could be drawn from the evidence available. Such phrases may at times be justified, but are also used to disparage the case of the opposition.

14) EITHER ... OR.

A oversimplified choice is presented, when actually there may be many alternative options available.

For example, it is proposed that either creatures were created in exactly the forms we see them today, or they evolved. As we have discussed, considerable variation within species or kind is possible, but not unlimited variation that could result in a totally new form of species.

15) DISTRACTION.

Attention is drawn away from the main issue to other matters, in the hope that the main item will eventually be forgotten.

It is not unknown for this to be used, in many areas of life. When faced with a problem, a writer may claim that he will show how it can be answered. Many pages later, after wandering over other topics, he might finish with a bold statement, which is not really a factual answer to the original problem.

16) 'AD HOMINEM'. (Against the man)

The attention is distracted from the weak case by attacking the credibility of the opposition.

This is an approach often resorted to by evolutionists who have labelled creationists with such descriptions as 'narrow-minded Bible-thumping fundamentalists who have to get their blinkered view of science from the Bible'. This draws attention away from any factual evidence that may be presented.

17) NAME CALLING.

This is to apply a dismissive or derogatory label to any of the ideas of the opposition in order to discredit them. Phrases used would be 'pure imagination', 'a flight of fancy', 'laughable'.

A phrase often used is 'so-called ... ', such as in ' ... the so-called human remains found in old strata'. This implies that that the remains are not really human, when actually all the evidence may point to the fact that they are.

18) THE FALLACY OF THE UNDISTRIBUTED MIDDLE.

This is a technical name that is best illustrated by an example. One would be — All humans are mammals — all monkeys are mammals — therefore all humans are monkeys. The fallacy is of course that man and monkeys are both within the circle that includes all mammals, but that does not mean that there is any connection between them — they are separate collections that are within a wider classfication (mammals). The fallacy in this example is clear, but it may be less obvious in an involved argument.

19) 'NON SEQUITUR' (It does not follow)

A line of reasoning is used in which the final conclusion is unrelated to the preceding arguments.
    An example is —
    Animals show a wide variety within one species. The family of Monkeys have a wide range of species. Therefore Man must have evolved from monkeys.
    To deduce evolution from varieties within quite different species is illogical, as well as being unproven.

20) SWEEPING STATEMENTS (Broad generalisations)

A claim is made that is too wide in its generalisation, and ignores the fact that there may be many exceptions to the rule.
    It may be asserted that 'All scientists agree that the theory of evolution is a proven fact.' This would of course ignore the not insignificant number who do not accept the theory.
    The making of sweeping statements is one that is used by many, even when it is known that there are a very small number of exceptions. There must, however, come some point when the number of exceptions is sufficiently large to invalidate the use of this phrase, at which point it is no longer used as a broad description, but as propaganda.

21) BLINDING WITH SCIENCE

The reader is treated to a barrage of scientific jargon in the hope that he will be suitably impressed with the erudition of the writer, and even though he is unable to understand them, he will nevertheless accept the writers conclusions.
    When Johansen discovered the handful of bones in Ethiopia that he claimed were a link between man and apes, he gave a detailed description of them in his report in 'Science' (26 January 1979). Typical of his description is 'Two pedal navicular bones ... exhibit

extensive cuboideonavicular facets and the pedal phalanges are highly curved' [15p217]. It is possible that Johansen felt that the highly technical scientific phraseology used in prestigious periodicals had to be matched by him in his description of a few scraps of bones.

22) QUOTING OUT OF CONTEXT.

A statement made by writer A is accurately quoted by writer B, but the impression it conveys is quite different to the views expressed by writer A. This misleading impression is usually achieved by writer B selecting only a specific passages and omitting other passages that qualify or override the statement made by A. Inclusion of these passages would have given a quite different understanding of A's views.

A creationist may say 'There does seem to be a great deal of evidence in support of the theory of evolution.' This could be quoted by evolutionists as an important admission. However, the following (unquoted) sentence might read 'It is only when this evidence is examined carefully that it is seen to be completely inadequate'. This second sentence completely overturns and corrects the impression given by the first.

23) SPECIAL PLEADING

A writer argues that the opposition should be excluded from presenting their case as they do not comply with the accepted norms of rational discussion.

This is the usual tactic to prevent creationists from even presenting their viewpoint. In their submission to the Supreme Court the American National Acadamy of Sciences said that Creation-Science is not science because

> ' ... it fails to display the most basic characteristic of science: reliance upon naturalistic explanations. Instead, proponents of 'creation-science' hold that the creation of the universe, the earth, living things, and man was accomplished through supernatural means inaccessible to human understanding.'
> 'Creation-Science' is thus manifestly a device designed to dilute the persuasiveness of the theory of evolution. The dualistic mode of analysis and the negative argumentation employed to accomodate this dilution is, moreover, antithetical to the scientific method.'

Creationism is thus to be disqualified even before the race has started. As evolution is the only other runner, it is able to romp home as a certain winner.

24) CONFIDENT ASSERTIONS

A statement is made with great confidence in the hope that the reader will be sufficiently impressed to accept what may be a very inadequate argument as a fully confirmed fact.

The clearest example of this is the claim that 'Science proves evolution', when true science does no such thing. There is the oft repeated anecdote of the speaker's notes which had written in the margin 'Argument weak — shout louder'!

25) GUILT (OR DENIGRATION) BY ASSOCIATION

By comparing or aligning the opposition with some contemptible situation or person, the degrading feature or guilt is transferred mentally to those they wish to decry.

An frequently used example is to decribe creationists as being as unscientific and as bigotted as 'flat earthers'. The intellectual superiority and scorn that most have towards flat earthers is thereby transferred to the creationist cause.

26) RIDICULE AND HUMOUR

This, in all walks of life, can be a very effective weapon against a superior opponent. Bernard Shaw used this frequently in his writings. This does not remove from us the responsibility, when the laughter has died down, to analyse what has been said and weigh it in the scales of Justice and Truth.

27) HURT FEELINGS

When discussing or debating with evolutionists, it may be pointed out that what they are putting forward is actually in error or just simply false. This may provoke an emotional reaction, and one might witness a display of anger. This could be taken as an indication that having failed to win the argument by common sense and reasoning, abuse is resorted to in order to change the line of the argument and put the discussion into a different atmosphere in the hope that the debating table may be turned by sheer force of words. This is not to say that this method is always deliberately used, although at times I feel that it is, but the resulting distraction is usually fairly effective in ending the discussion.

The best reply, if one can remain calm 'under fire', is to ask why a scientific subject, which evolution claims to be, should arouse such emotion for surely it is a matter of verifiable facts and not a matter of strongly held personal opinion that is not open to inspection.

28) THE APPEAL TO BE 'LOVING' AND 'CHRIST-LIKE'

In the course of strongly criticising evidence on any subject, particularly if it is claimed to be misleading or an outright falsehood, an appeal may be made that we should be 'loving' and more 'Christ-like' towards others of a different mind. This is of course perfectly correct, but there are times when this can be used simply to try to put the speaker into a poor light, obtain the sympathy of onlookers and gain the 'high moral ground'. This particular strategy can be used by Christians and non-Christians alike against anyone holding a controversial viewpoint and can be a very powerful counter-attack that silences any further argument — unless recognised and refuted.

It is by openly and frankly discussing the pros and cons of any particular viewpoint that the more truthful position may be revealed. If, on the other hand, theories are defended from a personal point of view then there is little hope of achieving this. Those who make this high moral appeal should be asked whether they are really intent upon finding the truth, or more concerned to defend a particular position.

What is being overlooked, at times deliberately, is that all Christians, of what ever persuasion, should be in search of the Truth, for Christ Himself said that He was Truth. We are rightly commanded to love our neighbour, but in defending the basics of the Christian faith, and to 'give a reason for the hope that is within us' [1 Pet. 3v15], we must also 'speak the *truth* in love' [Eph. 4v15]. To fail to do this is to be guilty of leaving our neighbour in the even greater danger of believing a lie, which is far from displaying true love for him.

We should note that on an important point of doctrine, the Apostle Paul corrected Peter and others *publicly* [Gal. 2v14f]. Errors must be dealt with openly whether within or without the Church.

....

Although I have provided as full a list of stratagems as I am able, I am not saying that they are deliberately employed by all evolutionists in order to justify their theory, for we can all be a victim of self-delusion. I do think, however, that there are many occasions when they are, for the frequency with which they occur in evolutionist's publications is far too high for coincidence. Writers on evolution have to be well versed in the art of sophistry, the dictionary definition of which is 'the use of false arguments intending to deceive'.

Creationists may well use the same methods without realising it, and no doubt the reader will want to examine this work with this in mind. I would venture to suggest however that their use by evolutionists would greatly outweigh their use by creationists.

It is in fact an interesting exercise to pick up any book on evolution and go through it carefully, rather like a detective, trying to spot where such stratagems are being used and where weaknesses in the case are being avoided by such means. In order to give some indication of just how frequently and subtly they are used we will briefly examine one popular book.

Dawkins' 'tricks of the advocate's trade'

Dawkins has written a popular exposition of evolution entitled 'The Blind Watchmaker' — the fallacious basis of which I have examined above in section III A 2. This is indeed a most suitable book to study as an exercise in spotting the use of deceptive stratagems, for the number of examples are prolific. Indeed, in examining this work, I was able to make additions to the list above of the stratagems available to writers.

Dawkins makes his method of argument clear as early as his Preface, for in this he says —

> 'Explaining is a difficult art. You can explain something so that your reader understands the words; and you can explain something so that the reader feels it in the marrow of his bones. To do the latter, it sometimes isn't enough to lay the evidence before the reader in a dispassionate way. You have to become an advocate *and use the tricks of the advocate's trade*. This book is not a dispassionate scientific treatise.'

Dawkins has at least forwarned us that he will be using every 'trick' (his word) to persuade the reader to accept his arguments. We cannot complain if we then fail to spot them when they are being imposed upon us. But does a really true proposition need the assistance of trickery to make itself fully understood? Surely it is only *false* cases that have to resort such means. There are many cases in Law in which a wrong verdict has been reached simply because one side was able to employ a 'clever' advocate. Dawkins, in his effort to be 'frank' with his readers, seems to have 'shot himself in the foot' with his opening statement.

He also mentions (p2) that 'There is little point in getting worked up about the way different people use words ... ' There is certainly a tendency in some philosophical works to become completely bogged down in hair-splitting definitions of words, but this does not arise in a popular work such as this. We must therefore be watchful of Dawkins' use of words to describe such broad concepts as 'life', 'mechanism', 'animal' etc. [Equivocation]. This will be made clearer later.

In one aspect at least, the book is what he claims it to be, for it is certainly ' ... *not* a scientific treatise.' Indeed, for a book dealing with a theory that purports to be based only upon 'scientific facts', their absence in this work is noticeable. The reason for this becomes clear in the first few chapters, for the book is mainly a philosphical argument that attempts to deal with Paley's 'watchmaker' analogy.

He begins with the words 'We animals ... ' [Broad generalisation], by which he is conditioning the reader to accept that he (together with Dawkins) is just an animal who is only a little more advanced than an ape. With equal accuracy he could have begun with 'We collection of chemicals ... '

There are also examples of Name-calling, where creationists are described as 'rednecked' (p251), and of Denigration by Association, for he considers the Genesis story 'has no more special status than the belief ... that the world was created from the excrement of ants.' (p316)

One of the main problems in criticising this book is the way in which he switches the line of his argument. He will go from a quotation to a philosophical argument, gives his very personal reactions to certain situations, redefines words, and uses many analogies. All this is done in a racy style that sweeps the reader onwards. Whilst some may find this approach convincing, I can only say that it can also generate a sense of bewilderment and an uneasy feeling that despite his prolific writing, he does not actually prove his point in a precise factual way. To the more critical reader, the whole book gives the impression of being one grand display of both the ploys of Distraction and Blinding with 'science'.

Much more could be written, but I would hope that even the little that has been examined is sufficient to expose the many stratagems that he warned us he would use. That many intelligent readers have found this work to be convincing is perhaps yet another subject worthy of debate.

FINAL COMMENTS

We have in this work considered some of the scientific evidence that contradicts the theory of evolution. This has received little publicity and as a consequence, the majority of people accept the theory as a 'proven fact' and express surprise that there is any evidence against it.

It must be admitted that there is considerable opposition to creationism — opposition that goes much deeper than the usual conflict between two scientific theories. This stems from the fact that the subject really under examination is that of the origin of life itself. To put it simply, the question is; has every living organism arrived by a series of chance combinations of chemicals or was it all designed and created by an omnipotent God? How we answer this question can have a fundamental effect upon the our concept of God and consequently upon the way in which we conduct our lives.

It is for this reason that creationists have met such strong opposition from those who either reject the concept of a creator God or will allow such a God only to work through the evolutionary process that has been 'proven by science'.

This whole subject of the assumed 'scientific basis' of evolution was neatly summarised in a privately circulated article I received from Philip Johnson who is Professor of Law at the School of Law, Berkeley, California. He wryly observed —

> 'Instead of a fact we have a speculative hypothesis that says that living species evolved from ancestors which cannot be identified, by some much-disputed mechanism which cannot be demonstrated, and in such a manner that few traces of the process were left in the fossil record — even though that record has been interpreted by persons strongly committed to proving evolution. A general theory of evolution so stated could just possibly be true, but surely a person is allowed to doubt.'

In view of the fact that the whole topic is subject to such powerful conscious and subconscious pressures, one can do little more than hope that the more thoughtful readers will be prepared to acknowledge that the evidence against the theory is at least worthy of their serious consideration.

Indeed, having considered the evidence and examined the way

in which the subject is publicised, there is no doubt in my mind that the theory of evolution should be considered as the greatest scientific hoax of all time. As I mentioned in the introduction, my main strictures are against those who consistently propogate the theory despite the considerable evidence against it. I would hope that having now reached the end of the book, that the reader may be more inclined to agree that such a judgement may well be justified.

SOME QUOTATIONS

Over the years, much has been written about the theory of evolution, both attacking it and defending it. In this section, we will examine first some confident statements by noted evolutionists, then some admissions, and finally some criticisms by scientists who are creationists.

1. CONFIDENT ASSERTIONS —

i) 'Of the *fact* of organic evolution, there can at the present day be no reasonable doubt; the evidences for it are so overwhelming that those who reject it can only be the victims of ignorance or prejudice.' [M. J. Kenny 'Teach Yourself Evolution.' 1966 p159]

ii) 'Darwin ... finally and definitely established evolution as a fact.' [George Gaylord Simpson.]

iii) 'the first point to make about Darwin's theory is that it is no longer a theory but a fact. No serious scientist would deny the fact that evolution has occurred ... all scientists agree that evolution is a fact ... there is absolutely no disagreement.' [Sir Julian Huxley, (grandson of Thomas Henry Huxley, the friend of Darwin) 'Issues in Evolution' vol 3 of 'Evolution after Darwin' Sol Tax editor, Chicago University Press]

2. SOME ADMISSIONS —

i) 'Not one change of species into another is on record ... we cannot prove that a single species has been changed' [Charles Darwin 'My Life and Letters']

ii) To suppose that the eye with all its inimitable contrivances ... could have been formed by natural selection, seems, I freely confess, absurd in the highest degree.' [Charles Darwin 'Origin of Species' Chapter 'Difficulties']

iii) The theory of evolution suffers from grave defects which are more and more apparent as time advances. It can no longer square with practical scientific knowledge.' [Dr. Albert Fleishmann, Zoologist of Erlangen University]

iv) 'There is not the slightest evidence that any of the major groups arose from any other' [Dr. Austin Clarke F.R.G.S. 'Quarterly Review of Biology' Dec. 28th p539]

3. CRITICISMS —

i) It is Darwin's habit of confusing the proveable with the unproveable which constitutes to my mind the unforgiveable offence against science.' [Dr. L. M. Davies 'The Bible and Modern Science' Constable 1953 p8]

ii) 'Evolution is baseless and quite incredible.' [Dr. Ambrose Fleming Pres. British Ass. advancement of Science in 'The Unleashing of Evolutionary Thought']

iii) 'Overwhelming strong proofs of intelligent and benevolent design lie all around us ... the atheistic idea is so nonsensical that I cannot put it into words.' [Lord Kelvin, Victoria Institute No. 124 p267]

D. CREATIONIST OGANISATIONS

The following is a list of the major creationist organisations that readers may be interested in approaching for membership or further information.

Creation Science Movement, (Formerly Evolution Protest Movement) 50 Brecon Ave., Portsmouth PO6 2AW. Founded in 1932, it was the first organisation to oppose evolution. Issues pamphlets, notices, holds meetings etc.

Creation Resource Trust, Mead Farm, Downhead, West Camel, Yeovil, Somerset BA22 7RQ. Suppliers of books, tapes, videos, leaflets etc. Also regular children's magazine in 'comic' style, and simple magazine for teenagers.

Mustard Seed Bookshop, 21 Kentish Town Road, London, LW1 8NH. Wide range of creationist books.

Biblical Creation Society, 51 Cloan Crescent, Bishopbriggs, Glasgow G64 2HN. Issues magazine 'Biblical Creation', holds meetings etc.

Torbay Christian Creation Topics, 9 Courtland Road, Shiphay, Torquay, Torbay TQ2 6JU. Cassettes, film shows, touring caravan exhibition etc.

AMERICA

Institute of Creation Research, 10946 Woodside Avenue North, Santee; P.O.Box 2667, El Cajon, California 92021, USA. Issues 'Impact' leaflets. Has travelling lecturers.

Creation Research Society, P.O.Box 15016, Terre Haute, Indiana 47803, U.S.A. Issues C.R.S. Quarterly giving scientific evidence for a young earth.

AUSTRALIA

Creation Science Foundation, P.O. Box 302, Sunnybank, Queensland 4109, Australia. Publishers of 'Ex Nihilo' and 'Ex Nihilo Technical Journal'. UK agency. P.O. Box 777, Highworth, Swindon, Wilts, SN6 7TU.

GERMANY

Wort unt Wissen, Voltastrasse 26, 2800 Bremen 33, Germany.

RUSSIA

Moscow Christian Creation Fellowship, Dr Dmitri A. Kouznetsov, Ph.D.D.Sc., The Protestant Inc. P.O. Box 83, Moscow 123290, U.S.S.R.

BIBLIOGRAPHY

1   Austin., S.A. 'Ten Misconceptions about the Geological Column' I.C.R.
     Impact article No. 137 November 1984.
2   Wonderly, D,. 'God's Time Records in Ancient Sediments' Crystal Press
     Michigan 1977
3   Austin, S.A., 'Were Grand Canyon Limestones Deposited by Calm and
     Placid Seas?' Inst. Creat. Research Impact Pamphlet No. 210 December
     1990
4   Gould, S.J. 'Wonderful Life' Hutchinson Radius 1989.
5   Glaessner, M. 'Precambrian Animals' Scientific American March 1961
6   Henbest, N. 'Oldest Cells are only Weathered Crystals' New Scientist v92
     n1275 15 October 1981
7   Gould, S.J., 'The Ediacaran Experiment' Natural History 93(2):14-23 (1984)
8   Sunderland, L.D.'Darwin's Enigma' Master Books 1988 p50-52.
     (Refers to 'Nature' 6 January 1983 and 'Science News' May 7th 1983
9   Burdick, C.L. 'Microflora of the Grand Canyon' Creation Research Society
     Quarterly 1966 v31 n1 p38-50
10   Burdick, C.L. 'Progress Report on Grand Canyon Palynology' CRSQ 1972
     v9 n1 p25-30.
     Also — Lubenow, M.L. 'Significant Fossil Discoveries since 1958:
     Creationism Confirmed' CRSQ v17 n3 December 1980 p158
     And — Lammerts, W.E.,'Are the Bristle-Cone Pines really so old?'
     Cr. Research Soc. Quart. v20 n2 p108-115 September 1983
11   Patterson, C., 'Evolution' Routledge and Keegan Paul in association with the
     British Museum (Natural History) 1978
12   'Origin of Species' Brit. Museum (Natural History) and Cambridge
     University Press 1981
13   Seagel, R.F., et al 'An Evolutionary Survey of the Plant Kingdom' Blackie
     and Son, London 1965
14   Karweil, J., Erdol und Kohle-Erdgas, Petrochemie 18th yr., July 1965 n7
     p565. Kolloquium Chemie und Physik dar Systinkhole.
15   Cherry-Garrard, A. 'The Worst Journey in the World' Penguin 1948
16   Weisburd, S. Science News 16 August 1986 p3: Also — Beardsley, T. Nature
     v322 p677 1986
17   Dewar, D., 'The Transformist Illusion' Dehoff Publications Tennessee 1957
18   Hayes, Quoted by Dewar in 'More Difficulties with Evolution Theory' p54
19   Kerkut, G.A., 'Implications of Evolution' Pergamon 1960
20   Simpson, G.L., 'Life in the Past'
21   Deperet, C., 'Transformations in the Animal Kingdom' p105.
22   Goldschmidt, R.B., 'The Material Basis of Evolution' Yale U.P. 1940
23   Halstead, B., 'Nature' 20th November 1980 v288
24   Bowden, M., 'Ape-men — Fact or Fallacy?' 2nd enlarged edition, Sovereign
     Publications 1981 (Reprinted 1988)
25   Newton, E.T., 'The Evidence for the Existence of Man in the Tertiary Period'
     Proc. Geologists Ass. v15 May 1897 p63-82.
26   Bowden, M., 'The Rise of the Evolution Fraud' Sovereign Publications 1982
27   Darwin, C., 'The Origin of Species' J.M. Dent and Sons. 1972
28   Murris, R., 'The Concept of the Species and its Formation' in 'Concepts in
     Creationism' Ed. Andrews E.H. et al. Evangelical Press 1986
29   Nordenskiold, E., 'The history of Biology' Tudor Publishing Co., New York.
     1928

30   Macbeth, N., 'Darwin Retried' Garnerstone Press 1974
31   Thimann, K. W., 'The Life of Bacteria' MacMillan Co. N. York 1955
32   Braun, W., 'Bacterial Genetics' W. B. Saunders, Philadelphia and London.
         1953.]
33   Sermonti, Prof G., Private communication and article 'On Industrial
         Melanism — Kettlewell's Missing Evidence' Rivista di Biologia, 77,
         No.1, 1984, 46-52
34   McLeod, K. C., 'The Sickle Cell Trait' Creation Research Society Quarterly
         v19 n1 June 1982.
35   Rusch, W.H. Snr.,'Ontogeny Recapitulates Phylogony' Creation Research
         Society Annual June 1969 v6 n1 p27-34
36   Barnett, S.A.,(Ed.) 'A Century of Darwin' Heinemann
37   Jarman, C., 'Evolution of Life' Hamlyn 1970
38   De Beer, G., 'Homology: An Unsolved Problem' Oxford Biology Readers,
         (J.J. Head and O.E. Lowenstein Eds.) No. 11, Oxford Univ. Press. 1971
39   Gruber, H.E. 'Darwin on Man' (2nd Edition) University of Chicago Press
         1981.
40   Lammerts, W.E., 'Why not Creation?' Baker Book House. 1970
41   Jones, A. 'Developmental Studies and Speciation in Cichlid Fish' Ph.D.
         Thesis. Zoology and Comparative Physiology Dept. Birm. Univ. Library.
         Diss. S2B72.
42   National Geographic Magazine, v 150, n 6 December 1976 (Fold out section
         on Whales)
43   Dewar, D., Merson Davies, L., and Haldane J. B. S. 'Is Evolution a Myth?'
         Evolution Protest Movement 1957.
44   Gower, D.B. 'Steroid Hormones and Evolution' Biblical Creation v6 n17
         Spring 1984 p149-159 (The Biblical Creation Society)
45   Scherer, S. 'The Protein Molecular Clock — Time for a Reevaluation'
         Evolutionary Biology 24 (1990) p83-106
46   Denton, M., 'Evolution: A Theory in Crisis' Burnett (Hutchinson) 1985
47   'The battery-operated duck-billed platypus' New Scientist 13 February 1986
         p25.
48   Dean G. et al, 'Defensive Spray of the Bombardier Beetle: A Biological Jet
         Pulse' Science. 8 June 1990 v248 p1219-1221
         Also — Rosevear, D. T., 'The Bombardier Beetle' Pamphlet No. 233
         Creation Science Movement.
49   Dewar, D. and Shelton, H.S., 'Is Evolution Proved ?' Hollis and Carter
         London 1947
50   Glover, J.W. 'The Human Vermiform Appendix — A General Surgeon's
         Reflections.' Ex Nihilo Technical Journal No. 3 1988.
51   Gitt, W. 'The Flight of Migratory Birds' ICR Impact pamphlet No. 159
         September 1986.
52   Able, K.P., Able, M.A. 'Calibration of the magnetic compass of a migratory
         bird by celestial rotation' Nature 27 September 1990 v347 p378
53   Croft, L., 'Early Life' Evangelical Press 1988
54   Green, D.E., and Goldberger, R.F., 'Molecular Insights into the Living
         Process' Academic Press, New York, 1967 (p407)
55   Hoyle, F., and Wickramasinghe C., 'Evolution from Space' Dent 1981
56   Aitken, A.J., 'Science Based dating in Archaeology' Longman 1990
57   Fisher, D.E. Nature Physical Science 19 July 1971 v232 p60-61
58   Funkhouser, J.G. and Naughton, J.J. 'Radiogenic Helium and Argon in
         Ultramafic Inclusions from Hawaii' Journal of Geophysical Research

15th July 1968 v73 n14 p 4601-7.

59 Hall, Prof. E.T. 'Old bones — but how old?' Sunday Telegraph 3rd November 1974 p15.

60 Fitch, F.J. and Miller, J.A. 'Radioisotopic age determinations of Lake Rudolph artefact site' Nature 18th April 1970 v226 p226-8 [also Nature 20th September 1974 v251 p213-215]

61 Curtis, G.H. et al 'Age of KBS Tuff in Koobi Fora Formation' Nature 4 December 1975 v258 p395-7.

62 McDougall, I. et al 'K-Ar age Estimate for the KBS Tuff, East Turkhana, Kenya' Nature 20 March 1980 v284 p230-4

63 McDougal, I., 'Ar40/Ar39 age Spectra from the KBS Tuff, Koobi Fora Formation' Nature 12 November 1981 v294 p120-4

64 Austin, S.A. Grand Canyon Lava Flows: A Survey of Isotope Dating Methods' ICR Impact pamphlet No. 178 April 1988.

65 Tilton, G. and Barreio B. Science v210 p1245-1247 198

66 Gleadow, A.J.W., 'Fission track age of the KBS Tuff and associated hominid remains in northern Kenya' Nature 20 March 1980 v284 p225-230

67 Knopf, A., 'Measuring Geologic Time' Scientific Monthly v85 November 1957 p225-236

68 DeYoung, D.B. 'Decrease of Earth's Magnetic Field Confirmed' CRSQ December 1980 v17 n3 p187-8

69 Sorensen, H.C. 'Bristelcone Pines and Tree Ring Dating: A Critique' Crea tion Research Society Quarterly June 1976 v13 n1 p5.

70 Hansen, S. 'Varvity in Danish and Scanian late-glacial Deposits' Danmark's Geol. Undersogelse 2 v63 1940 p423.

71 Berthault, G. 'Experiments on Lamination of Strata' Ex Nihilo Technical Journal volume 3 1988 (Previously appearing in C.R. Acad. Sc.Paris, t. 303, Serie II, no.17, 1986, pp.1569-1574)

72 Berthault, G. 'Sedimentation of a Heterogranular Material: Experimental Lamination in Still and Running Water' Ex Nihilo Technical Journal v4 1990 p95-102 (Previously appearing in C.R. Acad. Sci. Paris,t.306, Serie II, 1988, p717-724)

73 Barnes, T.G., 'Young age vs. geologic age for the earth's magnetic field' Creation Research Society Quarterly June 1972 v9 n1 p47-50 [also ICR Impact leaflets 100 (October 1981) and 188 (February 1989)

74 Morris, H. 'Does Entropy Contradict Evolution?' ICR Impact Leaflet No. 141 March 1985

75 A Setterfield, B., 'The Velocity of Light and the Age of the Universe' Creation Science Association (Australia) 1983
    B Norman, T. and Setterfield, B. 'The Atomic Constants, Light and Time' Stanford Research Institute International — an Invited Report 1987

76 Stanton, R.L., 'An Alternative to the Barrovian Interpretation? Evidence from Stratiform Ores' Proc. Australasian Inst. Min. and Met. n 282 June 1982

77 Young, D. 'Creation and the Flood' Baker 1977

78 Cox, D. 'Missing Mineral Inclusions in Quartz Sand Grains' Creation Research Society Quarterly June 1988 v25 n1 p54

79 A Gold, T. and Soter, S. 'The Deep-Earth-Gas Hypothesis' Scientific American June 1980 v242 n6 p130-137
    B 'Brontides: Natural Explosive Noises' Science 27 April 1979 v204 n4391 p371-375

80   Begley and Lubenow 'Gushers at 30,000 ft' Newsweek June 27 1988 p53
81   A   'Mantle Methane — Fools Gold?" Nature 25 November 1982 v300 p312-3
      B   Gold, T. 'Discussion of Asphaltene-like Material in Siljan Ring Well Suggests Mineralised Altered Drilling Fluid' Jour. Petroleum Technol ogy March 1990 p269
82   A   Kvenvolden, K.A., 'Methane Hydrate — A Major Reservoir of Carbon in the Shallow Geosphere?' Chemical Geology, 71 (1988) p41-51.
      B   Kvenvolden, K.A. and Kastner, M., '32. Gas Hydrates of the Peruvian Outer Continental Margins' Proc. of the Ocean Drilling Program, Scientific Results, v112 (Suess, E. et al., College Station, Texas Ocean Drilling Program)
      C   Ridley, I. and Dominic, K., 'Gas Hydrates Keep Energy on Ice' New Scientist 25 February 1988 p53-58.
83   Andrewartha, H.G., and Birch, L.C., 'The Ecological Web' Un. Chicago Press 1984
84   Elton, C. and Nicholson, M., 'The Ten-year Cycle in Numbers of the Lynx in Canada' J. Anim. Ecol. 1942 v11 p217-244
85   Krebs, C. 'Ecology: The Experimental Analysis of Distribution and Abun dance' Harper N.York 1985
86   Keith 'Role of Food in Hare Population Cycles' Oikos 1983 v 40 p385-395 Copenhagen
87   Smith, E.N., 'Which animals do predators really eat?' Creation Research Society Quarterly September 1976 v13 n2 p79-81
88   de Beer, G., 'Evolution' 3rd Edition, Trustees of the British Museum (Natural History) 1964

INDEX

By the same author

APE-MEN — FACT OR FALLACY?

A critical examination of the evidence highlights the very speculative theories based upon inadequate fossil evidence, and reveals the very dubious circumstances surrounding their discovery.

Summary of Contents

PILTDOWN. The considerable body of little-publicized evidence which incriminates Teilhard de Chardin S. J. *Professor Douglas' accusation.*
The involvement of the British Natural History Museum in the planning and execution of the hoax.

APE-MEN 'EVIDENCE'. The very speculative nature of the evidence for 'ape-men', and the presumptuous way in which this is presented.

EARLY HOMO SAPIENS. Their existence in deeper strata than those of 'ape-men'. The superficial reasons given by the experts for their rejection.

PEKIN MAN. A 25 ft. high ash heap, bone tools and other evidence of human habitation of the site virtually suppressed by the experts in China.
The appearance — and rapid disappearance in 13 days — of ten skeletons. Details of the later discovery of further human skeletons delayed for five years. Ape-like skulls reconstructed with human features. Investigation of the disappearance of the fossils at the time of Pearl Harbour suggests that they were found by the Japanese and passed to the Americans after the war, only to disappear again.

JAVA MAN. Dubois' concealment of human skulls for thirty years. The faking of scientific illustrations by Dubois' supporter, Professor Haeckel. The strange circumstances of the discovery of further fossil 'evidence' of Java man.

NEANDERTHAL MAN. The evidence that these were true men suffering from rickets, arthritis and syphilis.

THE AFRICAN APE-'MEN'. The admission by several experts that all these fossils are simply apes with no real human features.

  OLDUVAI GORGE. L. S. B. Leakey's discoveries examined.

  EAST RUDOLF. Richard Leakey's '1470' man really a human skull. How this 'awkward' fossil was quietly 'buried'.

  HADAR (Ethiopia). D. C. Johanson's meagre collection of fossils shown to be only those of apes.

  LAETOLIL. Mary Leakey's discovery of '3.6 million year old' footprints are clearly those of human beings. The evidence of similar tracks with those of dinosaurs in America.

CONCLUSION. The inadequacy of the fossil evidence for ape-men.
How the scientific establishment suppressed the publication of unwelcome evidence. *The basic motive for belief in the ape-men theories.*

*(*2nd Edition)*

Also published by Sovereign Publications

APE-MEN — Fact or Fallacy?

REVIEWS OF THE FIRST EDITION

English Churchman. 'This is a most learned, factual and highly-documented treatise on the subject of the findings, during the last two centuries, of certain ape-like fossil fragments from which scientists have deduced that man is descended directly from the apes.

The author exposes with pitiless logic and documentation the "last-word" theories of scientists, geologists and anthropologists, consequent upon the discoveries of such things as the "Piltdown Man", exposing many of them as frauds and hoaxes — which in the case of the Piltdown findings is now universally admitted.

This is a book of absorbing interest, especially to Christian teachers of Science and R.E., since any Secondary schoolboy will tell you glibly that "Man is descended from monkeys — Science has proved it." Mr Bowden's exposures are quite unanswerable ... '

International Catholic Priests Association. 'This is one of the most important works for years on the ape-men fossils, and it shines a bright light on four aspects. Firstly, the author shows that the ape-men fossils are dubious in the extreme. Secondly, he shows that evolutionists have concealed or minimized fossils of real men as ancient as these of their supposed ancestors, the ape-men. Thirdly, the ape-men have not been "discovered" by a huge army of scientists, but rather by a tiny group, numbered almost in single figures, travelling from hoax to hoax. Lastly, many will conclude from this work that right in the centre of this group was none other than Teilhard de Chardin ... This book is written by a clear thinker with a scientific approach who has long studied the original books and papers, weighed one account against another, and has now given us the results in a condensed yet clear way. Everyone should have this book and make sure that their public library also has it.'

Evangelical Times. 'In places it reads like a detective story ... Indeed one is left with the inescapable impression that the trail of suspicion goes beyond Piltdown ... [a book] which will be worth adding to your collection.'

Evangelical Action (Australia). ' ... Although written in a scholarly and technical manner, "Ape-men, Fact or Fallacy" is, nevertheless, quite easily understood by the non-technical reader and I recommend it to all those who, like myself, have to provide answers to evolutionary questions.'

Prophetic Witness (Review by Dr. F. A. Tatford). ' ... This is an important book, covering the whole ground of fossil evidence for evolution, and it cannot be ignored. We commend it to our readers.'

Fellowship (Review by Duane T. Gish, Ph.D. — Associate Director, Institute for Creation Research, California). 'Anyone interested in the fossil evidence for the ancestry of man should have a copy of Malcolm Bowden's book ... '

By the same author

THE RISE OF THE EVOLUTION FRAUD
(An exposure of its roots)
SYNOPSIS OF CONTENTS

SECTION 1 — Early Theories. Greek theories; the Dark Ages; the eighteenth Century; Linnaeus to Malthus.

SECTION II — Geology prepares the way. Hutton; Lyell; Murchison; Uniformitarianism — its rise and decline; criticisms by evolutionists.

SECTION III — The Rise of Evolution. Spencer; Huxley; Darwin a *Creationist* during *Beagle* voyage; his *failure* to notice variety of species on the Galapagos Islands; A. R. Wallance — fortuitous [?] timing of his letters; the falseness of the "first day sell-out"; critical review of "Origins"; the Huxley-Wilberforce debate — a different view of this "famous" event; evolutionists' dislike of mathematics; a portrait of Darwin the man; harsh childhood his main driving force to become famous.

SECTION IV — The Secret Aim — Achieved. Lyell's real motive of destroying the Biblical account of the Genesis Flood; his inducement of Darwin to write on evolution *after* his return to England; Darwin's anti-Christian statements; links between Evolutionist and Revolutionists (Malthus, Erasmus Darwin, Charles Lyell, Alfred Wallace); the powerful yet clandestine "X Club" which dominated the scientific world; Mendel's results deliberately ignored; present day barriers to Creationism by the Mass Media; criticisms of the BBC and the Marxist influence in the new exhibitions in the Natural History Museum.

SECTION V — Philosophic Criticism. The inherent contradiction in the 'scientific' evolution/materialist arguments; the inadequacy of Theistic Evolution.

SECTION VI — Implications and Applications. Moral repercussions; Nations — their God and 'quality of life'; the Future; Conclusion.

APPENDICES

I Darwin — A return to faith? **II** Criticisms of the Natural History Museum's new exhibitions. **III** Synopsis-Scientific evidence against evolution. **IV** Synopsis — The Ape-Men fallacy. **V** Synopsis — Scientific evidence supporting genesis. **VI** Creationist organisations. **VII** Quotable quotes for Creationists. **VIII** Famous Creationist scientists. **IX** Bible quotations. Bibliography. Index.

Also published by Sovereign Publications

FOREWORD

Having read Malcolm Bowden's outstanding book *Ape-Men: Fact or Fallacy?* several years ago, I was very pleasantly surprised to meet him recently at a Christian workers' conference at the Metropolitan Tabernacle in London, famous as Spurgeon's great church back in the nineteenth century. I had been speaking about the hidden background and modern impact of evolutionism, commenting on the need for some creationist scholar to make a thorough and original study of these two important subjects. Malcolm Bowden, after introducing himself, announced that he was then completing just such a manuscript!

This book is the product of his studies and is, indeed, a unique treatment of the remarkable phenomenon of evolutionism. In evolution we have a supposedly scientific world view for which there is no real scientific evidence whatever. Furthermore, it has spawned a vast complex of harmful philosophies and methodologies in the world during the past two centuries. Yet it is accepted and promoted, dogmatically and evangelistically, in the schools and universities of every nation in the world! Such a phenomenon surely warrants a more critical and incisive explanation than is now available in run-of-the-mill liberal treatments of the history and philosophy of evolutionary thought.

The Rise of the Evolution Fraud does, indeed, throw much new light on this remarkable epoch of history. Exploring the personal and environmental backgrounds of Darwin and his contemporaries, Malcolm Bowden has placed the whole subject in a new perspective. Especially significant are the new insights into Darwin's own psychological conflicts and the intriguing role played by the lawyer/geologist Charles Lyell in promulgating the rise of evolutionism. Bowden also adds a fascinating appendix on the question of Darwin's possible conversion to Christianity in the last weeks of his life. Finally, he provides an incisive critique of the logical basis of evolution, demonstrating its fatal scientific and philosophical weakness, as well as its devastatingly harmful impact upon society.

This book is bound to be controversial and will, no doubt, incur the vengeful wrath of the evolutionary establishment. In a sense it is still only an exploratory treatment, but its very publication should establish the need and stimulate the development of much further research in these highly important, but still dimly appreciated and understood, facets of modern evolutionary humanism. Evolutionism is far more than a mere theory of biology. It is a complete world view, with its roots extending far back through the entire history of man's rebellion against his Maker and with its deadly fruits entering the bloodstream of every field of human thought and activity today. It is vital that men and women somehow acquire a real understanding of its true character.

Malcolm Bowden has produced a book which can make a vital contribution toward that end. I am pleased and honored to commend it to the thoughtful study of readers everywhere.

Dr. Henry M. Morris
March 1982